ANCIENT ART · THE NORBERT SCHIMMEL COLLECTION

ANCIENT ART

THE NORBERT SCHIMMEL COLLECTION

Edited by Oscar White Muscarella

VERLAG PHILIPP VON ZABERN · MAINZ · W. GERMANY

Library of Congress Catalog Card Number: 73—19219

Printed in West Germany by Philipp von Zabern, Mainz

1974

A catalogue of a collection spanning more than 6 millennia of visual art created by artisans of many civilizations could not have been compiled without the help of eminent scholars.

We have tried to achieve more than a mere listing of antique objects. Through careful research of comparative material and citation of relevant bibliography our friends have produced a reference book that we hope will be a lasting contribution to the advancement of knowledge in the field of ancient art. Only inadequately can we express our indebtedness and gratitude for their guidance and friendship.

Special thanks goes to Oscar White Muscarella, the Editor, who supervised every phase of the production and gave the catalogue its shape and direction.

Evelyn and Norbert Schimmel

Table of Contents

Exhibition at
The Metropolitan Museum of Art
September 17, 1975 to March 1, 1976

Introduction

One of the main characteristics of the Norbert Schimmel Collection, aside from its beauty and cultural wealth, is that it has functioned as a public collection. No scholar, student, or interested layman who desires to see the collection or even one object has ever been denied access. Thus it serves the public and functions as a museum and is not considered to be one man's personal possession, selfishly shown only to a few close friends. Indeed, the fact that a new catalogue of the collection has now been produced is a continuation of the Schimmels' desire to make all the objects available to as wide an audience as possible.

The open spirited attitude of the Schimmels has resulted in a close relationship between them and many students and professional scholars concerned with ancient art and with archaeology from many parts of the world. Even where there are keen philosophical differences of opinion concerning the nature of private collections the friendships and mutual respect have continued. The scholars who have written for this catalogue applaud the generosity of the Schimmels and express their appreciation by contributing their work.

Aside from the authors, several people made this catalogue reach fruition. First there is Norbert Schimmel who worked with the editor for close to two years on all aspects of the production and who is solely responsible for the layout. Secondly, Herbert Hoffmann gave freely of his time and opinions based on his considerable editorial experiences, not the least being his editorship of the first catalogue of the Schimmel Collection. Joan Phelan, Mr. Schimmel's secretary, did all the final typing, too often working against deadlines and working from garbled drafts. A word must also be said for Franz Rutzen of Philipp von Zabern, Mainz, who cooperated enthusiastically throughout the planning work. He clearly understood the beauty and importance of the material entrusted to him for publication and the fine production of the catalogue is proof of his sensitivity and devotion to the collection.

Several objects published in the first catalogue have been omitted from this publication for the following reasons: Numbers 78 bis, 79 and 81 (old catalogue numbers) have been temporarily removed for laboratory tests. Number 35 has been demonstrated to be a modern forgery. Number 46 was stolen from a customs storeroom at Kennedy Airport and has not been recovered. Numbers 10 and 11 have been returned to the Greek Government when it was learned that they were stolen from a Greek museum. Numbers 18 and 29 were exchanged for other objects. Numbers 71, 84, 101, 108 and 124 were donated to museums.

Numbers 13, 19 and 39 are still in the collection but have not been included in this catalogue.

Oscar White Muscarella

Abbreviations

A K K E	Herbert Hoffmann, Ägyptische Kunst aus der Zeit des Königs Echnaton, Museum für Kunst und Gewerbe (Hamburg, 1965).
Akhenaten	Elenore Bille-de-Mot, The Age of Akhenaten (New York, 1966).
A R A C	J. D. Cooney, Amarna Reliefs from Hermopolis in American Collections (The Brooklyn Museum, 1965).
Art and Technology	Suzannah Doeringer, David Gordon Mitten, ed., Art and Technology: A Symposium on Classical Bronzes (MIT, 1970).
A B V	J. D. Beazley, Attic Black-figure Vase-painters (Oxford, 1956).
A R V²	J. D. Beazley, Attic Red-figure Vase-painters, 2nd edition (Oxford, 1963).
Brooklyn	C. Aldred, Art from the Age of the Sun King (Brooklyn Museum, 1973).
Fogg Museum Exhib. Cat.	Ancient Art in American Private Collections, A Loan Exhibition at the Fogg Art Museum of Harvard University, December 28, 1954 – February 15, 1955, arranged in honor of the Seventy-fifth Anniversary of the Archaeological Institute of America (Cambridge, 1954).
Hoffmann, Collecting	Herbert Hoffmann, Collecting Greek Antiquities (New York, 1971).
Jewish Museum Exhib. Cat.	Thou Shalt Have no Other Gods Before Me, Catalogue of an Exhibition held at the Jewish Museum, May 3 – September 6, 1964 (New York, 1964).
Kayser	Hans Kayser, Ägyptisches Kunsthandwerk (Braunschweig, 1969).
Master Bronzes	David Gordon Mitten, Suzannah Doeringer, Master Bronzes from the Classical World, Exhibition Catalogue Fogg Art Museum, December 4, 1967 – June 30, 1968 (Mainz, 1967).
Metropolitan Museum Exhib. Cat.	Dietrich von Bothmer, Ancient Art from New York Private Collections, Catalogue of an Exhibition held at the Metropolitan Museum of Art, December 17, 1959 – February 28, 1960 (New York, 1961).
N S I	Herbert Hoffmann, ed., Norbert Schimmel Collection (Mainz, 1964).
Queens College Exhib. Cat.	Man in the Ancient World, an Exhibition of Pre-Christian Objects from the Regions of the Near East, Egypt and the Mediterranean, February 10 – March 7, 1958 (Flushing, New York, 1958).
Roeder	G. Roeder, Amarna-Reliefs aus Hermopolis, Vol. II of Ausgrabungen der Deutschen Hermopolis-Expedition in Hermopolis 1929–1939 (Hildesheim, 1969).
7000 ans d'art en Iran	Sept Mille Ans d'Art en Iran, October 1961 – January 1962 Exhibition at the Petit Palais (Paris, 1961).
Sultan	Collection de feu Omar Sultan Le Caire (Paris, 1929).
Tadmor	Miriam Tadmor, Egyptian Art of the Amarna Period, The Norbert Schimmel Collection (Jerusalem, 1967).
Worcester Cat.	H. Tietz, Masterpieces of Etruscan Art, Exhibition Catalogue, Worcester Museum, April 21 – June 4, 1967 (1967).

Credits

The following scholars contributed to the Catalogue:

D. v. B. Dietrich von Bothmer, Metropolitan Museum of Art
J. W. B. Jill Waite Brinnon, Fogg Art Museum
J. D. C. John D. Cooney, The Cleveland Museum of Art
V. E. C. Vaugn E. Crawford, The Metropolitan Museum of Art
E. D. Ellen Davis, Department of Art, Queens College (CUNY)
S. D. Susannah Doeringer, Fogg Art Museum
A. G. Adolf Greifenhagen, Former Director of the Antikenabteilung, Staatliche Museen, Preussischer Kulturbesitz, Berlin-West
G. M. A. H. George M. A. Hanfmann, Fogg Art Museum
H. H. Herbert Hoffmann, Museum für Kunst und Gewerbe, Hamburg
P. O. H. Prudence Oliver Harper, The Metropolitan Museum of Art
D. G. M. David Gordon Mitten, Fogg Art Museum
O. W. M. Oscar White Muscarella, The Metropolitan Museum of Art
M. O'L. Michael O'Leary, Harvard University
L. A. S. L. A. Schneider, Archaeologisches Institut Hamburg
C. K. W. Charles K. Wilkinson, The Brooklyn Museum

Additions to the text and bibliography of the Ancient Near Eastern section published in the 1964 catalogue were made by O. W. M.

CLASSICAL ANTIQUITY

VESSELS OF TROY II TYPE

It was reported that these four vessels were found together. This is borne out by the close analogies of three of the vessels with those found by Schliemann at Troy, since assigned to the burnt city of Troy II g. These vessels are particularly important, since Schliemann's treasures, which he installed in Berlin, have been missing since World War II.

1   Lidded Vessel

The ovoid body with conical foot and cylindrical neck was raised from thick electrum plate; the bottom surface is concave, so the vessel rests on a rounded outer edge. The two handles, shaped like half cylinders, were formed separately and soldered to the wall. The lid, raised from a piece of electrum plate, is chamfered at its bottom edge and fits snugly over the tapering neck of the vessel. Holes drilled at the top and bottom of the two vertical projections on either side of the lid correspond to similar holes in the handles in order to accommodate a string handle for suspension. Numerous tool marks are visible on the surface.

The vessel is almost identical in shape to three slightly smaller silver examples found by Schliemann at Troy, and now assigned to Troy IIg. One of these vessels, with vertical fluting, had a similar concave foot, and another plain example had identical tubular handles. The shape is found exclusively in metal, although the Troy IIg stratum also yielded ceramic lidded vessels with the same system of tubular holes; one example had remains of the string handle preserved.

Electrum; Northwest Anatolian; Troy II period, ca. 2200 B.C.
Height with lid: 23 cm., without lid: 20.5 cm.; width at handles: 11.1 cm.; diameter of foot: 7.7 cm.; weight: 554.8 grams.

BIBLIOGRAPHY: Cf. Heinrich Schliemann, Ilios, The City and Country of the Trojans (New York, 1881), 469, nos. 783—784; cf. 214—215, nos. 23—25; 354, no. 252; Alexandre Rangabé, Atlas des Antiquités Troyennes (Leipzig and Paris, 1874), pl. 192, nos. 3490, a, b, Hubert Schmidt, Schliemann's Sammlung trojanischer Altertümer (Berlin, 1902), 229, nos. 5859—5860, 252, no. 6254. For the date: Carl Blegen et al., Troy I (Princeton, 1950), 207.   (E. D.)

2   Gilded Cup with two handles

The cup is constructed of separate parts, with a puzzling discrepancy between the body, which is of different more yellowish metal, and the handles and foot. The foot has been reattached in modern times. The body of the cup was raised from silver plate, with a round bottom, vertical offset neck, and the rim thickened and splayed outward. Thirty-one slightly concave vertical flutes begin at the offset of the neck and taper toward the bottom. The hollow foot was raised from silver plate with the bottom formed over a separate ring to provide a firm molding on which the vessel rests. The bottom is concave, and a round hole in the center indicates that a compass was used in the manufacture. The foot is now attached to the bottom of the bowl along a circular overlap, part of which is now missing. A single strip of electrum was overlaid by mechanical means on the round molding of the foot. A second strip of electrum covers the rim, forming a 1.2 cm. band outside and a 0.3–0.4 cm. overlap inside. The electrum is discreetly patched at two places on the rim; the identical appearance of the metal suggests that the patches were made during the manufacture of the vessel. The hollow tubular handles were applied last, over the gilding on the rim. They were constructed from pieces of silver plate, each folded into six vertical facets and soldered along its inner edge. The ends spread to form flat surfaces, triangular above and round below, which were soldered to the wall.

The cup is unique in shape, although many of its individual elements have parallels among the vessels from Troy II. The hollow tubular handles are a distinctive feature exclusive to Trojan metalwork; they were found on the gold sauceboat and a large silver tankard from Schliemann's Treasure A, and also occur on a silver "depas amphikypellon" in the British Museum that is said to have been found near Troy. The handles are closest of all to those of the sauceboat, which were formed with four vertical facets and with the ends flattened into the same triangular shape above and round shape below. The foot is very close to that of a gold cup from Treasure A, which was also formed separately, apparently over a ring, with a compass hole on the bottom. Similar fluting occurred on four of the vessels from Troy II, although with slightly flatter flutes. The Schimmel cup provides our first evidence that gilding was practiced at Troy, a technique known elsewhere at Ur and Alaca Hüyük.

Although the cup is unique in shape, it resembles, in its globular body and tubular handles, the tankards common in the Troy II period. Yet with its narrow offset rim and pedestal base, it also anticipates the kantharos, which did not appear until later in the Troy IV period. The cup appears to be, like the gold sauceboat, an inventive product

of the metalworker. The closest comparable examples in pottery are a cup with low ring base found by the University of Cincinnati expedition in the Troy IIg layer, and a cup with pedestal base but no offset rim found by Schliemann, apparently in the same layer.

Silver with electrum overlays; Northwest Anatolian; Troy II period, ca. 2200 B. C.
Height: 8.05 cm.; diameter: 10.5 cm.; weight: 427.5 grams.

BIBLIOGRAPHY: Cf. Heinrich Schliemann, Ilios, The City and Country of the Trojans (New York, 1881), 250–251, 465–467, nos. 772–773, 776–777, 779, p. 469, no. 784. Hubert Schmidt, Schliemann's Sammlung trojanischer Altertümer (Berlin, 1902), 229–232, nos. 5860, 5863–5865, 5873, p. 252, no. 6254. Friedrich Matz, Kreta, Mykene, Troja (Stuttgart, 1956), pl. 5. British Museum Quarterly 27, no. 3–4, (1963–1964), 79–80, pl. XXIX, B. AJA 71, 1967, pl. 10, c. Carl Blegen et al., Troy I (Princeton, 1950), 230, fig. 129, Shape A 46; Troy II (Princeton, 1951), 126, fig. 43, Shape A 37.   (E. D.)

3   Omphalos Bowl

This shallow dish was raised from one piece of silver plate. A hemispherical omphalos, 2.2 cm. in diameter, was impressed from the bottom and the vessel rests on its circumference. The upper edge was hammered to form a flat horizontal rim, 0.5 cm. wide, which projects beyond the wall both inside and out.
This vessel had a silver counterpart (now lost) in Schliemann's Treasure A (Troy IIg), but without the flat rim. However, copper examples with both omphalos and rim were found by Schliemann at Troy, and a silver example with the rim, omphalos, and a ring foot was recovered from the Troy IId level by the University of Cincinnati expedition.

Silver: Northwest Anatolian, Troy II period, ca. 2200 B.C.
Height: 3.0–3.4 cm.; diameter: 12.9 cm.; weight: 130.7 grams.

BIBLIOGRAPHY: Cf. Heinrich Schliemann, Ilios, The City and Country of the Trojans (New York, 1881), 469, no. 786; Alexandre Rangabé, Atlas des Antiquités Troyennes (Leipzig and Paris, 1874), pl. 189, no. 3458; Hubert Schmidt, Schliemann's Sammlung trojanischer Altertümer (Berlin, 1902), 231, no. 5868; 252, nos. 6255–6256; Carl Blegen et al., Troy I (Princeton, 1950), 210, 281, fig. 359, no. 36.449.   (E. D.)

4 Cup

The cup was raised from one piece of thick silver plate. It has round bottom and a ring foot that does not provide a stable standing surface. A carination 6 cm. from the rim divides the flaring concave upper body from the convex lower part. The rim is rounded but not thickened.

This cup has no counterpart among the metal vessels from Troy. That pottery versions are also lacking is not surprising since most Trojan metal shapes are exclusive to metalwork. The bodies of handled tankards from Troy III are sometimes similar in shape. More shallow carinated metal vessels without the flaring rim occur at Horoztepe. The closest comparable vessels are ceramic cups from Samos from the period contemporary with Troy II.

Silver; Northwest Anatolian; Troy II period, ca. 2200 B.C. Height: 10.0–10.7 cm; diameter: 12.1–12.2 cm; weight: 332.0 grams.

BIBLIOGRAPHY: Cf. Carl Blegen et al., Troy II (Princeton, 1951), pl. 9, nos. 34.403, 34.332, 34.381; Tahsin Özgüç, "New Finds from Horoztepe," Anatolia 8 (1964), 3, fig. 2; Vladimir Milojčić, Die prähistorische Siedlung unter dem Heraion, Samos I (Bonn, 1961), 23, nos. 3–4, pl. 14, 7–8, pl. 41, 9–10.   (E. D.)

5 Kernos

Coarse-grained reddish-brown clay interspersed with black impurities. Decorated with vertical and diagonal stripes in thin black glaze on a chalky ground. Seven small receptacles, presumably for offerings, are connected to each other and to the larger central cup by joints of clay, but there is no internal communication between the receptacles. This type of cluster vase with high conical stem seems to have been produced on the island of Melos.

Terracotta; Middle 2nd millennium B.C.
Height: 25.7 cm.

BIBLIOGRAPHY: Metropolitan Museum Exhib. Cat., no. 95 (with literature on Melian kernoi). Cf. CVA. Cambridge, pl. 6, 3 (ref. F. Eckstein).   (H. H.)

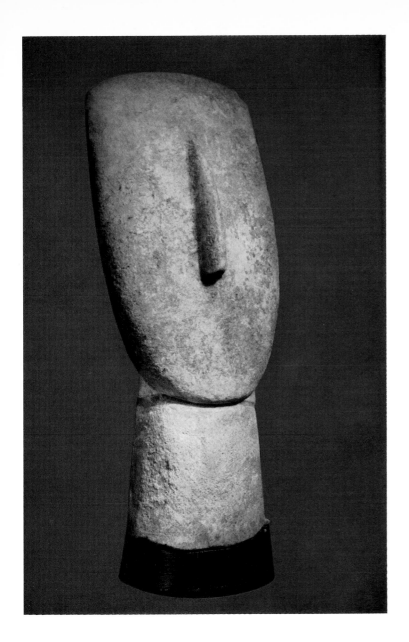

6 Head from a Cycladic Idol

The nose is indicated in "false relief", that is so say by abrading away the surrounding areas. The details of physiognomy were probably painted. A trace of the left shoulder is preserved.

Marble; 3rd millennium B.C.
Height: 17 cm.   (H. H.)

7 Female Cycladic Idol

The left foot is missing, and the head has been reattached. She stands with her legs together, separated by an abraded groove, her arms crossed below her chest and her head tilted back. Statuettes of similar style have been found on the island of Syros.

Marble; 3rd millennium B.C.
Height: 29 cm.

BIBLIOGRAPHY: Cf. C. Zervos, L'art des Cyclades, no. 254. (H. H.)

8 Female Idol

Tapering body with long cylindrical neck and head thrown back at a right angle. Two abraded clefts from the waist up and inward give the effect of arms bent at the elbows. Ears and nose indicated; pelvic area defined as a grooved triangle. One of a group of four said to have been found at Kirsehir in Western Anatolia; the others are in the collections of Alastair B. Martin, G. Schindler and the Museum of Primitive Art (Jewish Museum Exhib. Cat., no. 118).

Marble; Western Anatolian; probably 3rd millennium B.C.
Height: 10.8 cm.

BIBLIOGRAPHY: Metropolitan Museum Exhib. Cat., no. 87 (with other parallels, to which can be added Berlin [West], Staatl. Museen, 31457). J. Caskey, "The Figurine in The Roll-Top Desk," AJA 76 (1972), 192 f., pl. 44 (ref. N. Schimmel).

(H. H.)

9 Cycladic Jar

The jar, of a common Cycladic type, has four vertical lugs on its body. These have holes for the fastening of a cover, or, perhaps, for suspension.

Marble; 3rd millennium B.C.
Height: 8.7 cm.

BIBLIOGRAPHY: Metropolitan Museum Exhib. Cat., no. 93.

(H. H.)

BIBLIOGRAPHY: Cf. H. F. de Cou, The Argive Heraeum, II (Boston, 1905), 205–206, nos. 46, 47, pl. 77; C. Dugas, BCH 45 (1921), 350, nos. 24–26, fig. 10; P. de la Coste-Messelière, Delphes (Paris, 1943), 15, fig. 7; Richter, Handbook of the Greek coll. (Cambridge, 1953), pl. 13 f.; Ars Antiqua Auktion III (29 April 1961), 29, no. 66, and bibl.; H. Payne, Perachora I (Oxford, 1940), pl. 37:3; Master Bronzes, no. 25; Art and Technology, figs. 16—26.   (S. D. and D. G. M.)

11   Statuette of a Horse

The end of tail restored; head reattached. The horse stands on a rectangular perforated base, the bottom of which has been reinforced with two reverse scrolls of wire (see detail). A narrow rectangular projection from the rear of the base supports the tail. The ears, in relief, are small and drop-shaped; the eyes are not indicated. An unusual feature is the disc at the end of the muzzle.

Formerly in the collections of Otto Kahn and Sir Leigh Ashton.

Bronze; Greek; geometric period; 8th century B.C. Height: 7.5 cm.

BIBLIOGRAPHY: Cat. Sotheby, 23 May 1960, no. 215.   (H. H.)

10   Fanciful Bird

This comic bird forms an almost symmetrical U. Its giraffe-like head has slight swellings at eyes below an axe-shaped crest. Diagonal lines, in alternating groups of three, adorn its sickle-shaped tail. A triple-ridged collar marks the connection of body with tail and neck. One of the largest such birds known, it belongs to a group nicknamed "peacocks", although they probably represent poultry or large-crested birds such as the hoopoe. Their stylization is analogous to anatomical flattening in late Geometric horses. Most common in northern Greece, they also occur in central Greece and the Peloponnesus. Removal of extensive restorations on right of body has revealed that head, tail, and body were three separate fragments, and bared the fired core in the body with one of the chaplets that held it in place. The piece is the earliest known Greek hollow cast bronze with core.

Northern Greek (?), ca. 750–700 B.C.

Height: 14.5 cm., length: 18.5 cm., width: 3.2 cm.; hollow cast, dark green patina; pitting on body, light green spots on head and neck; right leg bent inward slightly.

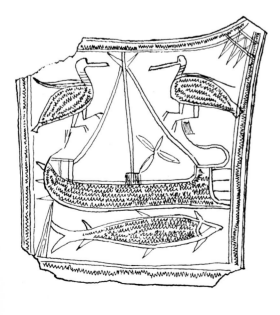

12 Fibula

Boat-shaped fibula of unusual size with large engraved catchplate.
On the front, a horse walking to the left and three water fowls. Vertical zigzags (a tether?) from the horse's muzzle to the corner of the picture. On the back, a ship, complete with ramming prow, deck cabin, mast, rudder, etc., over a large fish swimming in the same direction. Two large birds seem to perch on the mainstays, and a four-petal rosette occupies the segment formed by the mast and the forward stay. Both pictures occur also on two fibulas in Athens and London; the horse only on a fibula in Berlin.

Bronze; Boeotian; 8th century B.C.
Length: 18.2 cm.

BIBLIOGRAPHY: Auktion II der Ars Antiqua A.G., Lucerne, 14 May 1960, no. 113, (G. Hafner, with literature and discussion).   (H. H.)

13 Griffin Protome

Only the head of the monster – with the eyes and beak of an eagle, the ears of a horse (here greatly stylized) and the neck of a serpent – is preserved. Several such protomes would have been attached around the shoulder of a large cauldron, presumably to magically protect the contents against malevolent influence. Such cauldrons, together with the tripods on which they stood, have been found in the major sanctuaries of Greece and were a favorite form of votive dedication during the Orientalizing Archaic periods. The earliest known examples are of hammered sheet-metal construction and follow Near Eastern artistic conventions; this is a developed example of a *cast* protome.

The serpent scales have, as usual, been struck with a crescent-shaped puncheon. The white eye inlays have fallen out of their cylindrical sockets (depth resp. 1 and 1.5 cm.) at the bottom of which the original sand core of the interior ("lost wax" technique of casting) can be seen. The tips of the ears, top of the forehead knob, and the tip of the tongue are missing. A casting flaw in the right side of the beak has been repaired in antiquity with a hammered plug. This piece fits into Group V of the cast protomes as established by Ulf Jantzen.

Bronze; Greek; second half of the 7th century B.C.
Height: 13.8 cm.

BIBLIOGRAPHY: Cf. Ulf Jantzen, Griechische Greifenkessel (Berlin, 1955), 20 ff.; Master Bronzes, no. 65.   (H.H.)

The find, believed to be from Afrati (ancient Arkades) in South Central Crete, is divided between the Schimmel Collection, the collection of Mr. Nikos Metaxas, Iraklion, the Iraklion Museum, and the Museum für Kunst und Gewerbe, Hamburg. The Schimmel armor was previously exhibited in 1968 in the Fogg Art Museum's exhibition "Master Bronzes from the Classical World" and two years later in the exhibition "Dädalische Kunst auf Kreta" at the Museum für Kunst und Gewerbe, Hamburg. In as much as the entire find has been published in monograph form by H. Hoffmann and A. E. Raubitschek (Early Cretan Armorers, Mainz 1972, henceforth abbreviated as ECA), only a selection of decorated armor is published here. With the exception of a decorated cuirass in Hamburg, which is somewhat earlier than the rest of the group, the Afrati armor is homogenous and dates, according to this writer's published opinion, from the later seventh century B.C.   (H. H.)

14   Helmet with Horse and Lion

Two large confronting horse protomes in relief decorate each side of the helmet. On each cheek guard is an incised standing lion with canine muzzle and tail, facing in. Under the belly of the horse on the left side of the helmet, the dedicatory inscription:[Σ]υνήνιτος [τόδε] ὁ Εὐκλώτα ("Synenitos the son of Euklotas [took this]"). Both names appear to be of foreigners (ECA 15 f.). The verb and the demonstrative pronoun are omitted but can be inferred from similar inscriptions from other pieces of armor from the same find.
This helmet is connected by its inscription, as well as by the style of the representation, to the mitra, cat. no. 16. The two pieces of armor formed part of one and the same panoply, which may have included a cuirass likewise decorated with an equine motif.
Recomposed from many fragments and some missing areas are restored in plastic. The frontlet is missing (the imprint and rivet holes remain).

Height: 24.5 cm.

BIBLIOGRAPHY: Master Bronzes, no. 20; Dädalische Kunst auf Kreta, A2; ECA, H2.   (H. H.)

15 Helmet with Winged Youth

The figure decoration, executed in a combination of repoussé work and incision, shows virtually identical scenes
on each side: two winged youths holding intertwined serpents between them. The center of the serpent composition
is formed by a roundel which originally held an applique
(traces of solder remain). Under the serpents' tails (on
one side of the helmet only) is an incised and sippled
double-bodied panther. On the front of the helmet, above
the visor, the traced inscription: Νεόπολις ("Neopolis").
According to A. E. Raubitschek, Pollis, the legendary
founder of the Cretan city of Lyttos, may be meant ("New
Pollis"), in which case we can assume that the dedicator
of the helmet was a Lyttan.
Various mythological interpretations have been offered
for this unique representation (ECA 34 ff.). In my opinion the "duplicated" serpent tamers on the Schimmel helmet belong in the realm of Cretan folk religion. They take
their place among the various demons of oriental origin
in the service of major Hellenic deities with which Archaic
Crete abounded.
The helmet is worked in two halves joined (riveted) by an

overlapping seam. The frontlet, with repoussé rosettes, is separately applied. The neck guard is ornamented with a register of incised hatched dog-tooth pattern over a register of tongues with double outlines. The lateral terminations consist of a palmette on a curving stem. The incised rosette on the round flanges of each cheek guard were originally covered with an applied repoussé rosette, the oxidized remains of which have been removed. As-

sembled from many fragments, the missing parts are restored in plastic. Two wire loops, fore and aft, secured the ends of a crest.

Height: 21 cm.

BIBLIOGRAPHY: Master Bronzes, no. 29; Dädalische Kunst auf Kreta, H 1; ECA, H 1 (full discussion and literature).

(H. H.)

16 Mitra with Horse Protomes

Facing horse protomes in relief occupy nearly the entire height of the field. The inscription is as on the helmet preceding (with the exception that the demonstrative pronoun τόδε is here furnished), indicating that the two pieces of armor form part of one and the same panoply.

On the function of mitrai, as stomach shields to protect the wearer against arrows, see ECA, 9 f.

Preserved intact.

Height: 15.4 cm.; diameter: 24.2 cm.

BIBLIOGRAPHY: Master Bronzes, no. 31; Dädalische Kunst auf Kreta, A 9; ECA, M 1; Hoffmann, Collecting, colorplate 4.   (H. H.)

17   Mitra with Winged Horse Protomes

Confronting horse protomes with sickle-shaped wings, in relief-supplemented coarse incision. The composition creates a rotating windmill effect.

The inscription is along the rim: Αἰσονίδας τόνδ᾽ ἧλε ὁ Κλοριδίο ("Aisonidas the son of Kloridios took this"). While Aisonidas is a Greek (probably Cretan) name, Kloridios appears to be foreign. See ECA, 15 f.

Missing: left suspension ring and parts of the rim; left horse head creased.

Height: 15.4 cm.; diameter (as preserved): 24.2 cm.

BIBLIOGRAPHY: Dädalische Kunst auf Kreta, A 10; ECA, M 2.

18   Mitra with Sphinxes

Two stiff-legged confronting sphinxes in low relief and fine incision, their heads, crowned by tall *poloi*, turned to face the beholder. Their hindquarters rest against the upcurve of the panel frame. From the base of each polos headdress "floats" an incised palmette on a long stem. The sphinxes have short dedalic "perukes", and each wears a crescent-shaped amulet on a neck band. Uninscribed.

John Boardman has explained the prevalence of sphinxes in the art of Afrati-Arkades through the influence of North Syria, with which this city entertained close commercial and cultural connections. Sphinxes carry fallen warriors from the battlefield on the early metopes from Mycenae, and perhaps their "sinister" aspect made them particularly suitable as armor decoration.

Restored: parts of the rim; missing: two suspension rings.

Height: 17.4 cm.; diameter: 22 cm.

BIBLIOGRAPHY: Master Bronzes, no. 32; Dädalische Kunst auf Kreta, A11; ECA, M 3.

19 Hydria Handle

Dull blue-green patina; remains of the casting-core visible at top and bottom. Vertical central handle of a hydria. The hollow-cast shaft is decorated with a female head in high relief. The shaft spreads towards the top and is surmounted by two addorsed lions which served, by means of rivets through their haunches, to fasten the handle to the hydria rim. At the bottom of the handle, flanking the female head, a pair of horse protomes, also in high relief, merging into a flat terminal palmette.

The female has a sharp nose and chin and a narrow upturned mouth. Her eyes are almond-shaped and the brows emphasized by notching. Her hair is arranged in three rope-like braids on either side of the face and two across the forehead. Above the latter rises a tall polos of vertically bundled rods. A heart-shaped amulet on a band is carelessly engraved on her neck.

The style of this handle has been related of the Grächwil Hydria (Berne) and the Metapontum Tripod (Berlin), two works generally believed to have been made in Tarentum, South Italy, around the middle of the sixth century B.C. The polos and the amulet indicate that the female head is that of a goddess, most likely Artemis as πότνια θηρῶν, or Mistress of the Beasts (as on the Grächwil Hydria). Artemis as Protectress of Horses has also been suggested (by Herbert Cahn).

Formerly in the Doria collection, Capua.

Bronze; Tarentine; ca. 560 B.C.
Height: 21.6 cm.

BIBLIOGRAPHY: H. Hoffmann in AJA 68 (1964), 185 ff., pl. 163, 1; H. Jucker, in Antike Kunst 7, 1 (1964), 6, compares this bronze to a handle in Pesaro and argues that both works are Laconian; Master Bronzes, no. 72; BdI 1881, 145 f. (ref. H. Jucker); H. Jucker, Bronzehenkel und Bronzehydria in Pesaro (Pesaro, 1966), 91 ff., pl. 35.

(H. H.)

20   Handle and Spout of a long-beaked Jug

The handle, cast separately from the neck of the vessel, consists of a twisted, double-stranded shaft terminating at its bottom end in a plate formed by a stylized five-petalled palmette flanked by snakes' heads, and at its top by a female protome wearing a high polos. The rope-like portion of the shaft terminates at both ends in a double annulation, the upper one of which is ornamented by beading. The top of the handle continues its upper surface into a narrow thumb rest which at its front end becomes the polos of the protome; its sides are decorated by tongues topped by beading. The handle is intact, as is the spout, except for its missing tip. The female protome exhibits a pronounced nose, developed chin and small, pursed mouth; the bulging, almond eyes are marked by pupils produced by blows of a ball-headed puncheon (noted by H. Hoffmann). The ears are double volutes. The hair is waved back, parted in the middle and horizontally notched along the sides. Beading and notching are visible above the hairline. The rear surface of the protome is flat and undecorated, bifurcating at the bottom to provide a more secure attachment to the neck of the vessel. Below the protome, rotelles project to either side; the outer surface of each one displays a row of small punched circles around the periphery, with a single punched circle at the center.

This handle and spout originally belonged to a type of bronze jug sometimes called a *prochoos*; two large intact jugs of this form, of late archaic date, have recently been excavated at Vitsa, in Epirus. In addition, two closely similar handles, in the National Museum, Athens, featuring twisted handles, attachment plates in the form of palmettes flanked by snakes, and female protomes wearing poloi, were recovered from Dodona. D. K. Hill had suggested that these two handles might be Attic in origin, reflecting influences from East Greece. In view of the discoveries at Vitsa, however, an Epirote or southern Macedonian workshop now seems to have been the source for several of the archaic examples of this handle type, including the Schimmel handle. It is instructive to compare the protome on this handle with that at the base of the Schimmel hydria handle, no. 19, thought to be Tarentine in origin but considerably earlier than this piece.

The corrosion products have been largely removed, leaving a thin olive-green patina. Widespread pitting of the surface is due to minute gas bubbles formed during the casting. The neck spreads slightly; its bottom is decorated with a scalloped flange topped by a delicate plait that looks like a wire added to the surface, although it is an integral part of the casting. Traces of solder adhere to the underside of the neck; there is no trace of rivetting.

Bronze; Greek, Epirote or southern Macedonian, ca. 520 B.C.
Length of handle: 15.8 cm.; width of palmette: 4.6 cm.; diameter of spout: 4.7 cm.; height of spout: 12.4 cm.; width of female protome: 4 cm.; height of female protome with hair and polos: 5.2 cm.

BIBLIOGRAPHY: Cf. D. K. Hill, "The Long-Beaked Jug in Greek Lands," AJA 66 (1962), 57–63. Spouted bronze jugs from Vitsa (Ioannina Museum): P. M. Frazer, Archaeological Reports, 1968–69 (1969), 22, fig. 23, especially right-hand jug; I. Vokotopoulou, Archaiologikon Deltion 22, B2 (1969), 349, Πιν. 253, βιγ. Handles from Dodona: Hill, op. cit., 58, nos. 4, 5; 60; pl. 16, fig. 12 (no. 5). I am indebted to Herbert Hoffmann for many of the technical and stylistic observations about this handle cited here.   (D. G. M.)

21　Couchant Goat

The goat reclines with its forelegs tucked under its body and its head turning to the left. The underside of the body is hollow. A number of details – oval eyes, eyebrows, right nostril, and casual strokes in the beard – are incised. The inner sides of the ears, which curve forward, are concave up to the neck.

A number of such reclining, hollow-cast goats are known; they adorned the rims or shoulders of deinoi, kraters, tripods and other large vessels. Good examples of such goats on vessels come from late sixth century B.C. graves at Trebenischte. Often claimed as Corinthian products, these goats, along with many other kinds of cast decorative vessel attachments, were most likely made in numbers by several metalworking centers throughout mainland Greece.

The surface appears to have been mechanically cleaned in modern times.

Bronze; Greek; Peloponnesian?, late sixth to early fifth century B.C.
Length: 9 cm.; width (front to back of head): 3.5 cm.; height: 6 cm.

BIBLIOGRAPHY: Cf. D. M. Robinson, AJA 59 (1955), 20, figs. 4–5; Münzen und Medaillen, Auktion 26 (5 October 1963), no. 11, pl. 4; Master Bronzes, no. 63, p. 71 (Vassar College Classical Museum; head turned backward); for examples from Trebenischte, B. Filow, Die archaische Nekropole von Trebenischte (Berlin, 1927), 53–54, pls. 52–54.　　(D. G. M.)

22　Cheese Grater in the Form of a Goat

An amusing object, well adapted to its function – the grating of cheese (which in ancient times was produced almost exclusively from goat's milk). The goat has been cast in one with the solid rectangular base on which it stands. This is pierced with eight holes for the rivets securing the grating sheet, which was also fastened to the base by folding up the edges (now mostly broken away). Only the essential capric details are given: strong horns curving backwards, jutting ears, goatee and small flat tail curling back over the body. Such cheese graters were often placed in tombs. Curiously, they are usually found in male tombs only. Cf. Jacobsthal in Athenische Mitteilungen 57 (1932), 1 ff., Beil. 1–2 (kindly called to my attention by Erika Simon, who discovered this charming piece on the New York art market). Only two other such graters are known to me: British Museum 1929 8–11, in the shape of a horse, and one in the shape of a stag, supposedly from Asia Minor, on the New York art market. Others no doubt exist.

Bronze; from Asia Minor; 6th–5th centuries B.C.　　　　　　(H. H.)
Height: 7.7 cm.

23   Seated Monkey

This solid cast monkey is seated with his body bent forward, feet together, and right arm extended in front of him. His left arm is bent in toward his head in a gesture that resembles *aposkopein* ("Looking far off"), often seen in statuettes of satyrs and Pan. Fingers and toes are shown by incisions; the thumbs project from the paddle-shaped hands. Vertical striations represent hair on the monkey's head; similar incisions on the right side of the torso show the outline of ribs. Notches on the insides of the feet may have been caused by a pin or nail that attached the figure to a base.

Seated monkeys of this sort, while uncommon, are known among Greek bronzes. Three bronze monkeys in Berlin are said by Neugebauer to be Peloponnesian types. A handle attachment with a monkey, from the sanctuary of Artemis Orthia at Sparta, also has the left hand held to the head. N. Schimmel cites a bronze attachment from Dodona in the National Museum, Athens, in which a monkey squats, holding his right hand to his head, on a palmette between two horse protomes; there is a loop at the back of the attachment. The style of the horse protomes suggests a date late in the sixth century B.C. Earlier, seated ape and monkey-like creatures appear among the small bronzes of the late Geometric period. While their function and meaning, which Neugebauer has seen as apotropaic, remains uncertain, Greek monkeys may well have been inspired by simian subjects in Egyptian art.

Bronze; Greek, late archaic, perhaps Peloponnesian, ca. 550–500 B.C.
Height: 4.3 cm.; length (front to back): 4.3 cm.; width (across elbows): 4.2 cm.

BIBLIOGRAPHY: For monkeys in classical times, cf. W. C. McDermott, The Ape in Antiquity (Baltimore, 1938); K. A. Neugebauer, Katalog der statuarischen Bronzen im Antiquarium. I. Die minoischen und archaisch griechischen Bronzen (Berlin/ Leipzig, 1931), nos. 186—188, pp. 87—88, Taf. 29; R. Dawkins et al., Artemis Orthia, 202, pl. 90 f.; for *aposkopein*, cf. I. Jucker, Der Gestus des Aposkopein (Zürich, 1956).   (D. G. M.)

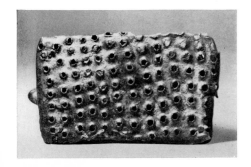

24 Winged Boar

He stands at bay on a narrow and slightly convex rectangular plinth with his forefeet set foreward and his head lowered to meet the attack. His large sickle wings project upward at the shoulders on which small overlapping feathers are indicated with puncheon marks. The bristles on his long mane and jaw are carefully incised.

A round hole in the horizontal strut between the wings, and continuing down through the body, must originally have held a rod, indicating that the object served as a support. The curvature of the plinth and the emblematic nature of the subject tempt one to conjecture that the piece may be the crest holder of a helmet, or possibly the support of a candelabrum or thymiaterion.

A precise dating is difficult; it may be as early as ca. 550 B.C. The stylistic conventions are virtually identical with those canonical for boars on Early and Middle Corinthian pottery; the wings too are of a type current in the first half of the sixth century B.C. A date in the second half of the century seems to be warranted by the developed modelling of the haunches, which can hardly be early Archaic. Fifth century Greek boars have more pliant muzzles with eyes more deeply imbedded in the skull. Moreover, the winged boar, an orientalizing conceit adapted from Near Eastern fantastic animals, becomes virtually extinct after the Archaic period.

No less problematic is the question of geographic origin. As pointed out by Payne, the winged boar is an Ionian type. On the other hand, the absence of the break in the center of the spinal bristles, as well as the taut modelling and rich use of incision, argue against Ionian origin. The one known parallel for the Schimmel bronze is from Spain but may well be an import.

The wild boar plays an important role in mythology. It is sent by angry gods to devastate the countryside and is eventually subdued by a hero (e.g. Theseus, Herakles). It stands for male prowess and valor. In the Iliad the combat of two great warriors is likened to a combat between a boar and a lion. The significance of boars and winged boars as shield devices is probably to be seen in this general context.

Bronze; Greek; probably second half of the sixth century B.C.
Height: 5.5 cm; width: 5.3 cm.

BIBLIOGRAPHY: Acquired from the Münzen & Medaillen A.G. Basel (Bern Art and Antiquities Fair 1968, hectograph list no. 114). The boar in the Hispanic Society, N.Y. is published in Archäologischer Anzeiger 1941, col. 207, fig. 5; Garcia y Bellido, Hispanica Graeca 2 (1948), 28, 95–96, no. 13 (references by Dietrich von Bothmer). For another close parallel (somewhat later and without wings): D. K. Hill, Catalogue of the Classical Bronze Sculpture in the Walters Art Gallery (Baltimore, 1949), no. 275. On the wild boar in Greek sculpture: G. M. A. Richter, Animals in Greek Sculpture (New York, 1930), 23 f.; on Archaic gems: J. Boardman, Archaic Greek Gems (Evanston, 1968), nos. 498–501; in Greek art of the Orientalizing period: H. Payne, Necrocorinthia (Oxford, 1931), 70, note 3. On the imagery of boars and lions in Archaic Greek Art: F. Hölscher, Die Bedeutung archaischer Tierkampfbilder (Würzburg, 1972). (H. H.)

24 bis   Mirror support

A naked girl, of whom only the upper part is preserved,
stands frontally. The right arm, bent at the elbow at right
angles, is straight and presumably held a fruit or flower
in the hand that is now missing. The left arm, also bent at
the elbow, is pulled back, and the hand, likewise missing,
may have been close to the left thigh holding a pome-
granate. She wears a necklace with a pendant and over her
right shoulder a band to which amulets are attached. Her
long hair falls on her back in ten tresses that reach to the
end of her shoulder blades. In front her hair hugs the forehead, with one short tress falling in front of her left ear
and two in front of her right ear. She also wears a diadem
that terminates in a volute at each end. The mirror disk

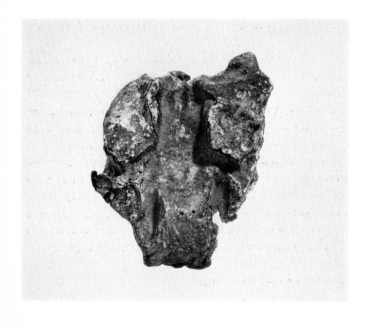

proper, now missing, was supported by a sturdy flange to which it was soldered. In addition, its position was steadied by a leaf-shaped attachment in the back that still has the two rivets. The flange terminates at each end in a scroll. These are linked to the shoulders of the girl by galloping sphinxes whose heads are crowned by poloi. The entire support was cast in one piece.

The mirror support was found lying with its back encased in a lump of molten lead.

The bronze belongs to a small class of mirror supports of which there are two examples in the Metropolitan Museum of Art, one in Athens, from Amyclae, one in Munich, from Hermione, one in Vienna, and one in Sparta. The class has last been discussed by Theodora G. Karagiorga in Deltion 20, 1 (1965), pp. 96 ff.; useful, too, is the article by Camillo Praschniker in JOAI 15 (1912), pp. 219 ff.

Bronze; Greek (Peloponnesian?); third quarter of the sixth century B.C.

Height, as preserved: 9.23 cm.   (D. v. B.)

25 Pan   This statuette of a nude Pan is more rustic than no. 25.[bis] He stands on his left leg; the right leg is raised but connected with the plinth by means of a notched strut. Both arms are stretched out and the hands are open with the fingers curved as if they held something. The mouth is open as if singing. The two horns of a goat are attached to a small cap on the crown of his head. The goat's tail is very short, as is the goatee.

The carving is crude: the inside of the legs is quite flat, as is the underside of the caprine lower legs. The shoulder blades continue their sweep around the sides right into the breasts. Incised lines indicate the spine, the separation of the buttocks, and the sternum. The hair on the chest, the pubic hair, and the hair on the upper legs is incised. The back of the upper legs is decorated with purely ornamental lines. The top of the horns, the edge of the cap, the contour of his hair in back, the eyebrows and the mustache are notched. Nipples and navel are engraved.

For the gesture of the hands and the general composition the statuette may be compared with one in Leipzig, known to me only through the line drawing in Salomon Reinach, Répertoire de la statuaire grecque et romaine vol. 4 (1913), p. 38, fig. 9. F. Brommer has drawn our attention to two very similar statuettes, both unpublished, of which one is in Istanbul and the other in Ankara: both are of the same scale as Mr. Schimmel's and look as if all three at one time formed a group, perhaps attached to the rim of a cauldron or to another vessel or utensil.

Bronze; Peloponnesian; perhaps late fourth or third century B.C.
Height, with plinth: 13.0 cm.   (D. v. B.)

25 bis Pan

The goat-legged creature is shown in a dance. Since he wears the *phorbeia*, the mouth-strap of flute-players, the gesture of the two hands may be interpreted as holding two flutes or a syrinx and something else. His eyes give the appearance of being closed, though this may be due to the cursory modelling.

Save for the two horns, the ears, and the goatee, his face is more human than is common with Pan. The caprine part of his body begins with the hips and the groin.

In spite of several unfortunate breaks that result in missing extremities, the modelling in its rustic simplicity comes through splendidly, and the style is consistent throughout. The pectoral muscles repeat the sweep of the shoulder blades, and the hair on the head is arranged in tiers, in the same fashion as on the legs.

Bronze. Peloponnesian. Late fifth or fourth century.
Height, as preserved, 13.1 cm.

BIBLIOGRAPHY: On representations of Pan in art see F. Brommer in Pauly-Wissowa Realencyclopädie suppl. 8 (1956) cols. 949–1008. Bronze statuettes of Pan are surprisingly rare. To the list given by Brommer add Boston 99.490 (M. Comstock & Cornelius Vermeule, Greek, Etruscan & Roman Bronzes [1971] p. 73, no. 75) and three once in the Basle market (Münzen und Medaillen AG Auktion XXII, 13. Mai 1961 pl. 18, nos. 60–61; Auktion XXVI, 5. Oktober 1963 pl. 7, no. 23; the first of these is now in the Basle museum). I. Jucker, Der Gestus des Aposkopein figs. 22–25 illustrates three bronze statuettes of which two (Louvre Br. 4292 and Sofia 3755), though previously listed (had not been illustrated before), and D. K. Hill, Classical Bronze Sculpture in the Walters Art Gallery pl. 19, nos. 77–79 publishes three bronze statuettes in Baltimore, all three presumed to be Roman.

David Mitten has discovered that the best comparison for the Schimmel statuette can be made with one in Lyon. Though somewhat smaller in scale and different in stance, the Lyon statuette (Stephanie Boucher, Bronzes grecs, hellénistiques et étrusques [Sardes ibériques et celtiques] Lyon, 1970) p. 22, no. 6, shares with the Schimmel bronze the treatment of the human anatomy and the convention for the caprine hair.   (D. v. B.)

26   Statuette of a Warrior

Tip of sword and ends of helmet crest missing; head reattached. An Iberian bronze statuette of great rarity and importance. The warrior, naked but for his cap-like helmet, draws his sword which hangs from a baldric. His shield arm has been accidentally bent towards his body, imparting a greater degree of torsion than was originally intended. Characteristically Iberian features are the oval face with small eye-, mouth- and ear-slits, the bulging and low-slung pelvis and the disproportionately short and wobbly legs – also the diminutive round shield with central boss attached directly to the end of the arm-stump.

Bronze; Iberian; 6th century B.C. (?)
Height: 10.5 cm.

BIBLIOGRAPHY: Cf. F. Alvarez-Ossorio, Catalogo de los exvotos de bronce ibericos (Madrid, 1941), pls. 126, right bottom (for the head), 98, right (for the body) and 146 (for the shield).   (H.H.)

26 bis   Horseman

The youth is naked but for the fillet in his hair. His fists are pierced, the raised left having held the reins, the right, which rests on his thigh, a riding crop *(kentron)*. His hair is treated as a smooth cap from which six parallel plaits fall on his shoulders and halfway down his back. The underside of his thighs are hollowed for a snug joint with the horse's back.

In general, the strength of this bronze lies not in the rendering of detail but in the elegant transitions of the various sculptural planes. The pronounced shoulder torsion is rare in rider bronzes of this period; compare the (possibly Italic) bronze rider in the Museo Correr, Venice. The influence of Ionian style may be detected in the boy's oval facial features which contrast with the sparse and angular – truly Spartan – style of his body. The neck and right ankle are cracked; the left foot and right side of the face are damaged.

Bronze; Greek; Laconian; late third quarter of the sixth century B.C.
Height: 9.5 cm.

BIBLIOGRAPHY: Cf. M. Comstock – C. Vermeule, Greek Etruscan and Roman Bronzes in the Museum of Fine Arts (Boston, 1971), nos. 32–33; Master Bronzes, no. 58, and the literature there given.   (H.H.)

27 Herm

Plinth bent up at the front corners and broken off at the right; bright malachite patina. This is the "Warren herm", found at Hagios Sostis in Arcadia. The ithyphallic pillar stands on a low rectangular platform in two steps. "The bearded head ... has a merry twinkle in his eye as if amused by his own prowess" (Hanfmann); his hair is neatly combed in a fringe around the forehead, with long tresses falling down his back and over the shoulders in front. Hair, beard and moustache are rendered by scoring the wax model; there are relatively few traces of tooling directly on the bronze. The small oblique hole through the left arm of the herm has never been satisfactorily explained; perhaps it served for the attachment of a talisman.

A close stylistic parallel to the "Warren herm" exists in the bearded man with a stick in the Watkins Collection (Fogg Museum Exhib. Cat., no. 211, pl. 65), which likewise is probably Arcadian and influenced by the school of Argos. At first, the herm on its severe pillar makes a very early impression; close study, however, tends to bear out the rightness of Lullies' and Schefold's contention that this, the most beautiful of bronze herms, was probably not made before 490 B.C. and possibly even a decade later.

Bronze, solid cast; Arcadian; ca. 490 B.C.
Height: 9 cm.
Formerly in the collections of E. P. Warren, E. Langlotz, and G. Ortiz.

BIBLIOGRAPHY: H. Licht, Sittengeschichte Griechenlands I (Dresden, Zurich, 1926), 217 (ref. C. Vermeule); E. Langlotz, Frühgriechische Bildhauerschulen, pl. 41 c; Crome, Athenische Mitteilungen 60–61 (1935–1936), 303, note 3, pl. 107; R. Lullies, Typen der griechischen Herme, 13, 3; Auktion 11 der Münzen und Medaillen A.G. Basel, 1953, no. 293; Fogg Museum Exhib. Cat., no. 210, pl. 62; K. Schefold, Meisterwerke Griechischer Kunst, 222 (Basel–Stuttgart, 1960). Cf. also the small unpublished marble herm in Boston, acc. no. 08.537, a work of about 425 B.C.

(H. H.)

28 Top of a Kerykeion (Herald's Staff)

The snake emblem of Hermes, the messenger god, is supported by a short Doric column. The interlinked heraldic serpents have beards and coxcombs. A punched circle appears at each corner of the entablature; the same puncheon was employed to render the serpents' eyes. The column has two holes at the bottom and must originally have been affixed with a nail or cross pin to a wooden rod. A good dozen kerykeia (lat. caeducei) dating from the Classical period of Greek art are known. A number of them bear votive inscriptions, indicating that they were also dedicated in sanctuaries (by the public officials whose badge they were?). Other serpent kerykeia are in the museums of Dallas, London and Palermo.

Bronze; later sixth or early fifth century B.C.
Height: 18.7 cm.

BIBLIOGRAPHY: For the most recent discussion see H. Hoffmann, Ten Centuries that Shaped the West. Greek and Roman Art in Texas Collections (1970), no. 78, as well as H. Hoffmann – A. E. Raubitschek, Early Cretan Armorers (Mainz, 1972), no. 34 (and note 5 on the imagery of intertwined serpents). (H. H.)

29 Rampant Lion

Rampant lion with head turned right to face the beholder. Reddish-green patina, deeply pitted; right ear and rear paws missing. Originally perhaps part of the handle attachment of an elaborate volute krater (on the analogy of the Vix krater. Cf. R. Joffroy, Le trésor de Vix). He would then have been standing within a framework of floral scrolls. This hypothesis, at any rate, would explain the fluted and slightly curving rod (broken off at both ends) which our lion grasps between his front paws. No close parallels for this lion are known to me: the Baker lion (Metropolitan Museum Exhib. Cat. 134), with which this animal sculpture has been compared, is probably South Italian and nearly a century earlier. Despite the simplified and Archaic-looking treatment of the anatomy, several features, including the naturalistic fall of the mane, the "feathers" of fur on the forelegs and the mock-ferocious countenance, tell us that the date of our lion must be sought towards the end of the fifth century, if not at the beginning of the fourth.

Formerly in the collections of the Duke of Leeds, B. W. J. Kent, Esq., A. van Branteghem, J. Hirsch, and G. Ortiz.

Bronze; Greek, possibly Corinthian; ca. 400 B.C.
Height: 11.5 cm.

BIBLIOGRAPHY: Hess A.G. sale, Lucerne, 7 Dec. 1957 (Hirsch Collection), no. 46, where the bronze is stated to be South Italian. (H. H.)

30 Gorgoneion

A relief in thin bronze (bluish green patina) worked repoussé, with details, such as the eyes, teeth, cheek wrinkles and the cleft in the tongue, engraved. The slight convexity of the object leads one to think that it might be a shield emblem, although the small size would be unusual. Compare the shield device in the form of a gorgoneion figured on a black-figured vase-fragment from the Acropolis: Graef-Langlotz, pl. 63, 1021.

Bronze; Greek, perhaps Attic; ca. 500 B.C.
Diameter (max.): 7.4 cm.   (H. H.)

31 Satyr Mask

Handle-attachment of a situla. The mask was fastened to the vessel by three rivets, which are preserved: two through the rotelles and the third through the satyr's chin. The fan-shaped beard has a fine wave-line striation. Said to be from Gordion, Anatolia.

Bronze; Greek; early 5th century B.C.
Height: 10.6 cm.   (H. H.)

32   Bronze Mirror with Hinged Cover

The hinge and the small carrying handle formerly attached to it are missing, but the correspondences of mirror and cover in both the dimensions and the corrosion assure the pertinence of the cover to the mirror. Also missing is the small loop that was once fastened to the relief on the cover and permitted the easy opening of the mirror. The rim of the cover is broken in places and parts of it are lost.

The cover is decorated on the outside by a large bust of a woman in profile to right. She wears her rich hair in the fashion that archaeologists have dubbed "melon coiffure". Her jewelry is added in silver: a twisted earring that may have terminated in an animal's head and a plain necklace.

The inside of the cover is engraved and shows an Eros and a woolly satyr. Both are dancing to right but are out of step. The satyr wears a fillet and an ivy wreath in his hair and has slung his cloak over both upper arms. In his right hand he holds a torch. Eros has bracelets, an anklet, and a chain with small pendants over his left shoulder. His long hair is tied with a long ribbon. The ground on which both figures dance is rendered with short hatched lines. The figures and the ground were once silvered and stood out sharply against the golden color of the highly polished bronze background: of the silvering only traces remain in the engraved lines.

Of the two-hundred-odd bronze mirrors with hinged covers that are known, only about thirty-five have an engraved decoration on the inside. The subject matter of these engravings, if not purely ornamental, is usually taken from the world of women, and, not surprisingly, Eros predominates. Often he is shown by himself or with Aphrodite: to see him with a satyr is novel. In the fifth century B.C. the domains of Aphrodite and of Dionysos are still kept apart, but in the fourth century they merge and overlap, and many instances of this can be found on contemporary South Italian vases.

The mirror is more easily dated by the engraved design than by the head in relief. The Eros is particularly close to Boston 01.7514 (Comstock and Vermeule, Greek, Etruscan, and Roman Bronzes in the Museum of Fine Arts, Boston, p. 256, no. 368), and to London 292 which Züchner (Die griechischen Klappspiegel, p. 14) has convincingly dated in the third quarter of the fourth century B.C.

Diameter of mirror: 16.93 cm.; diameter of cover: 17.386 cm.; thickness of the mirror with the cover placed on it: 4.98 cm.   (D. v. B.)

33 Relief Mirror

Preserved with hinge and suspension loop. The lid is decorated with a farewell scene in applied relief. A female figure, clad in a girdled chiton and mantle, which she has let fall to her lap, is seated on a rocky knoll. She extends both arms towards a youth, placing her left hand lightly on his right shoulder and supporting his forearm with her right hand. The youth, who wears laced boots and a chlamys thrown over one shoulder, leans on a tomb pillar and extends his right arm absently in response to the woman's more dramatic gesture. The setting appears to be in a rustic sanctuary, and an air of sorrow, reminiscent of a grave relief, pervades the scene.

Part of faces are restored. Otto Brendel first identified the scene represented as Orestes and Elektra at the tomb of Agamemnon (verbally).

Bronze; Corinthian; 2nd half of the 4th century B.C.
Diameter: 13 cm.

BIBLIOGRAPHY: J. D. Cooney "Deluxe Toilet Objects", Bull. Cleveland Museum of Art, Sept. 1973, 215–221.   (H. H.)

34   Mirror with Siren Handle

The mirror disc rests directly upon struts projecting from the head and elongated wings of a siren, from the feet of which once projected a handle. Bronze hand mirrors decorated with sirens, while popular throughout the Greek world during the second half of the fifth century B.C., reached their greatest elaboration in the Greek cities of southern Italy and Sicily.

Bronze; Greek (allegedly from Asia Minor), ca. 450–425 B.C. Height: 26.5 cm.; height of siren: 10 cm.; diameter of mirror disc: 19 cm.

BIBLIOGRAPHY: Master Bronzes, no. 105; cf. P. Oberländer, Griechische Handspiegel (Hamburg, 1967), 150–178.   (D.G.M.)

35 Hephaistos

Hephaistos stands with his weight on his right leg, his left leg drawn back. He wears the short blacksmith's tunic, fastened across the left shoulder and with a gather above the waist; the skirt extends to just above the knees. He extends his right arm diagonally away from his body, with elbow bent and forearm held horizontally. The right fist still grips the remnant of a separately fashioned and inserted rod. The left shoulder is noticeably higher than the bare right shoulder; the cloak is fastened over it with a circular brooch. The cloth of the hem of the garment falls over in a fold at waist height under the right arm.

The fabric of the cloak is defined by shallow parallel grooves on front and back; they converge on the front from the waist to between the legs. The folds are more massive and less sculptural on the left side. On the back, they flare out over each leg, effectively modelling the swelling outlines of the buttocks beneath.

Hephaistos is barefoot. In his left hand, held hanging parallel to his side, but bent outward slightly, he cradles what appears to have been a pair of tongs. The tool held in his right hand was most likely a hammer. The index finger of his left hand is extended along the base of the tongs, while thumb and other three fingers wrap around and steady the handles of the tongs. These three fingers appear to have been defined or at least retouched after the casting. Hephaistos' thick neck and powerful shoulders are carefully rendered. His massive head, framed in a squarish border of curly beard, has been cast with precise attention to details unusual in so small a statuette. His mouth is prominent beneath a spreading, curly mustache. His wide eyes, with drilled pupils, look out from beneath prominent, arched eyebrows; his cheekbones are high. His hair forms a uniform fringe around his head, projecting from under his conical *pilos*. The *pilos* has a short roll in back, just above the hair on the nape of the neck, which is textured with a series of short parallel grooves.

This statuette, monumental in conception and detailed in execution despite its miniature scale, is one of the finest versions yet discovered of the bronze cult statue of Hephaistos made by Alkamenes, Phidias' most celebrated pupil, late in the fifth century B.C. for the Temple of Athena and Hephaistos at Athens. The statues of the two gods, patrons of arts and crafts, especially metalworking, stood side by side in the cella of the temple, which stood on the hill of Kolonaios Agoraios, part of the Athenian industrial quarter, overlooking the Agora from the west. With the aid of representations from the minor arts, especially the relief discus from a Roman lamp in the National Museum, Athens, Semni Karusu has succeeded in re-constructing the basic form of the statue of Hephaistos. The god stood with his weight on his right foot; his upraised left hand grasped a long staff or scepter, while his outstretched right hand held a hammer. The creator of the Schimmel Hephaistos has altered the pose by lowering the left arm to grasp a pair of tongs, thus concentrating attention upon the god's role as metalworker. This pose is closely parallel to that of a bronze statuette in the Greek royal collection, Dekelia, published by S. Karusu and on a glass paste gem in Berlin; this statuette, however, is much more elongated and shows a pronounced swing to the right hip, in contrast to the stockier proportions and serene, monumental air of the Schimmel Hephaistos. The Dekelia statuette wears boots that fasten above the ankle. While Karusu posits a second statue as the prototype for the Dekelia statuette, it seems unnecessary to assume more than a free adaptation of Alkamenes' original for both the Dekelia and Schimmel bronzes. The organic, monumental quality of the Schimmel statuette, along with the maker's painstaking attention to detail, suggests to the writer that it is the product of a classicizing workshop faithful to the spirit of the original but not yet reduced to merely academic reproduction. The folds of the tunic lack the dry, harsh linearity often produced by tooling after casting which is characteristic of so many bronze statuettes of Roman date. An appropriate place for manufacture would be Athens itself; perhaps the statuette was a votive offering for the cult of Hephaistos, or a miniature souvenir of the famous cult statue. The Schimmel statuette stands midway between its monumental prototype and a number of Roman bronze statuettes of Vulcan, a magnificent example of which exists at Geneva.

The right foot is broken off above the ankle, otherwise the statuette is intact. It has a dark reddish-brown metallic patina and some abrasion on the left side of chest.

Bronze; Greek, Hellenistic, late third or early second century B.C., perhaps cast at Athens. Height: 9.4 cm.; width: 6 cm.

BIBLIOGRAPHY: For the basic study of the cult statue by Alkamenes, cf. S. Papaspyridi-Karusu, "Alkamenes und das Hephaisteion", Athenische Mitteilungen 69/70 (1954/55), 67–94; the Dekelia statuette: S. Karouzou, "Statuette d'Hephaistos en bronze", Revue Archéologique (1968 : 1), 131–138; glass paste in Berlin: E. Diehl, AA (1963) 749 ff.; Statuette of Vulcan in Geneva, Musées d'Art et d'Histoire 19229; Master Bronzes, no. 257, p. 267.   (D. G. M.)

36 Squatting Negro

A Negro boy, naked but for a cloth wrapped around his waist, is shown squatting in listless boredom on a rock, his knees drawn up to his chin. His head, tilted to one side, is cupped in his left hand. His right hand, on which rests his chin, is placed limply over his right knee. The little sculpture is a perfectly compact and "closed" composition. The rock is open at the bottom.

The ethnic, probably Sudanese, traits and the characteristic squatting pose (which the Greeks considered undignified) indicate that the figure represents a slave. More specifically he is the faithful manservant waiting patiently to escort his master home. The bronze has a smooth dark green patina.

A number of similar statuettes are known (all of inferior quality). They have been termed "Alexandrian", but on insufficient grounds. Babelon-Blanchet, Bronzes antiques ... de la Bibliothèque Nationale, no. 1012, squats on a conical mound and has been interpreted as an "inkwell cover" because of a round hole between the boy's feet. The reason for the hole becomes apparent through the comparison with a similar bronze figure on the London market (Syme): the latter has a silver penis. Oxford B67 EF and Oxford 1971.886 will shortly be published by Michael Vickers who brought them to my attention.

Bronze; solid cast; Late Hellenistic period.
Height: 7 cm.

BIBLIOGRAPHY: Hoffmann, Collecting, figs. 70 a, b.   (H. H.)

37 Horse Head from a Couch

The head boards of Hellenistic klinai (couches) were decorated on each side with a projecting animal-head sculpture. Mules and horses were particularly favored, but other types of animal head finials, including panthers, Molossian hounds and even elephants (Munich, Antikensammlungen) are known.

The free rendering of the mane, as well as the sensitive modelling of the muzzle make it apparent that this horse head is a Hellenistic Greek original, closely related in style to the horse heads of the celebrated couch discovered in the excavations of Priene in Asia Minor (Th. Wiegand and H. Schrader, Priene [Berlin, 1904], 378 ff., figs. 480 f.).

For the appearance of a typical Roman horse-head couch finial cf. AJA 61 (1957), 167 ff.

The base of the neck is covered by a panther skin terminating at the front in a stylized panther mask, and below this is a projecting shell-shaped ornament that forms the transition to a profiled frame that originally would have contained a flat inlay panel. At the top of the panther skin are the oxidized remains of an iron nail by which the finial was fastened to the wooden bed frame. The horse's eyes were originally inlaid with silver; the teeth are separately indicated by incision. The head is partially covered with blistering oxide incrustation; there are minor restorations on the frame and on the back of the panther skin, the lower part of which has been twisted.

Bronze; Greek, second century B.C.
Height: 18.5 cm

BIBLIOGRAPHY: Cf. G. M. A. Richter, The Furniture of the Greeks, Etruscans and Romans (London, 1966), 107 ff.; A. Steinberg, in Master Bronzes, no. 147. Cf. also C. L. Ransom, Couches and Beds of the Greeks, Etruscans and Romans, (Chicago, 1905), 34 ff. and plates. (H. H.)

38 Wineskin Balsamarium

This unguent container is in the form of a filled pigskin tied at the neck with a cord. The animal's naval, pizzle and tail are suggested by three knobs. The container, an askos, can be set on its rump when not in use. A tenon at each side of the neck, held in place by the cord, is pierced at the top and formerly held a suspension ring (only one ring is preserved). There is a solid-cast stopper, the top of which is rendered as a grape leaf with the stem bent forward so as to serve as a loop for a third ring which probably held a safety chain.

A Hellenistic black-glazed plastic guttus in the Ashmolean Museum, Oxford (Inv. 1947.246); called to my attention by Michael Vickers) helps to date and interpret the Schimmel balsamarium. It has the form of a filled wineskin with an infant Eros seated on its back tieing up the neck with a cord. Other bronze wineskins: Athens N. M. 13218, from the Peloponnese, lenght 14 cm. (M. Vickers); Art Museum, Indiana University (D. G. M.).

The two counter-wound wire rings of the balsamarium reproduce a common type of Hellenistic earring. The bronze has a glossy dark green (malachite) patina.

Bronze; said to be from Asia Minor; Hellenistic period.
Height: 12.7 cm.   (H. H.)

39 Pygmy

A phallic dwarf with bald pate, long moustache and beard in four curly strands
stands with legs spread far apart and brandishes a throwing stick (now bent)
with his right hand. His clenched left fist, extended sideways at shoulder height,
may perhaps be thought of as grasping a crane by the neck (Iliad III, 6).

The conception of the pygmy as a bald and bearded phallic gnome seems here
to be conflated with the iconography of Beş, the Egyptian dwarf god of cosmetics
(cf. H. Bonnet, Reallexikon der ägyptischen Religionsgeschichte [1952] 101 ff.),
suggesting that the origins of the motif may be Alexandrian.

His hair is treated in cap-like fashion with closely spaced blows of the ball-head
puncheon (suggestive of tight curls). His physique is characterized by a steatopygous rump, short puttyish legs, knotty muscles and – typical for dwarfism –
abnormally developed chest and shoulders.

Bronze; Etruscan (?); third – second century B.C.
Height: 5.8 cm.

BIBLIOGRAPHY: Hoffmann, Collecting, fig. 71 a–b. A number of replicas and near
replicas of this small sculpture are known: Copenhagen, National Museum, from
Orvieto (Bildertafeln des etruskischen Museums [1928], pl. 109); Baltimore, Walters Art Gallery (D. K. Hill, Cat. Bronzes, no. 156, pl. 33 = Teitz, Worcester Cat.,
no. 96); Boston, Museum of Fine Arts; C. Vermeule, Cat. Bronzes (1971), no. 132.
Bologna, Museo Civico. Cf. also Reinach, RS. 564. F. Rumpf, (Gnomon 1929 639)
first recognized the type to represent a pygmy. On the meaning of phallic
dwarfs and "grotesques" in Greek art cf. the article "Phallos" in Pauly-Wissowa,
Reallexikon XIX, 1744 ff.   (H. H.)

40   Funerary or Votive Relief

An elderly bearded man of powerful build is shown seated to the right on what appears to be a ledge or rock-cut throne. His feet are supported by a low mound or outcropping of the ground. He is clad in a long mantle which he has draped so as to leave his right shoulder bare. His left hand clasps a short staff; his right hand is placed on his right knee.

Much about this relief is unusual, and in the absence of an inscription it is difficult to decide whether it is a funerary or a votive monument. The seat is uncommon, and normally the man's feet would be supported by a footstool θρῦνυς as on a related relief in Ince Blundell Hall (E. Berger, Das Basler Arztrelief [1972], fig. 49–50). Both details appear to be significant – i.e., dictated by the nature of the subject – and not to be explained as "abbreviations" or "provincialism". The man's short staff, spreading at the top, is obviously more of a badge or attribute than a practical aid in walking. It appears in similar form on another relief that has, in the past, been cited as a comparison for ours: Copenhagen, Glyptothek Ny Carlsberg, from Rhodes (Berger, note 254, fig. 120). Both the Ince Blundell and the Copenhagen reliefs pose the same problem: votive or funerary? As regards the identity of the person represented, his stooped posture, eloquently expressive of advanced age, would seem to rule out a divinity. Yet the very unusual nature of his "natural" seat suggests that he is not an ordinary mortal, who would be depicted on a chair (κλισμός), folding stool (δίφρος ὀκλαδίας) or, in case of high rank, a throne (θρόνος) (cf. Richter, The Furniture of the Greeks, Etruscans and Romans [1966], 13 ff.). I would venture to suggest that a local sage or hero is represented, although the possibility that a wandering physician is portrayed need not be excluded (cf. Berger, 97, 151 ff.).

A few technical observations regarding the original context seem warranted. The relief of the "mound" under the man's feet is clearly discernible down to the

bottom of the slab, so that the slab could not have been let into a base block. All four lateral edges retain their ancient smooth dressed surface; the back is flat and roughly worked. Two ancient drill holes of ca. 5 mm. diameter in the top edge, one of them retaining an oxidized bronze pin, apparently served to fasten the relief in its ancient frame, the top of which may have had the form of a small pediment. This would explain the lack of edge profiles on any side and the fact that the man's head projects above the upper termination of the slab. In Asia Minor the facades of many rock-out tombs were once studded with separately worked reliefs imbedded in this manner, and, as pointed out by Berger, the custom may have been more universal (Berger, 9).

Although the fine details are almost entirely washed out, suggesting long exposure to the elements, enough remains to permit of some conclusions regarding the style. The fastidiously carved moustache and spade-shaped beard, as well as the elongated feet remind one of the physician relief in Basel (Berger, Arztrelief); the stylized treatment of the himation at the shoulders, describing an almost perfect circle, recall the famous tomb relief from Orchomenos in Boeotia (with which the Basel stele has been compared), signed by the sculptor Alxenor from Naxos (Berger, fig. 46). While sharing certain similarities with these works the Schimmel relief is more provincial than either of them – witness the almost flat treatment of the arm, the heavy and inarticulate folds of the himation – suggesting Asia Minor, the Cycladic islands, or even Thasos – the provenience connected with it – for the origin of its style. The evidence of the marble (see below) might be cited in support of any of these attributions.

Greyish marble of coarse crystalline structure; the surface is weathered and "sugary". Fragments are missing from the bottom; modern drill holes exist in the top and bottom (one and two respectively).

Greek; said to have been found at Thasos; perhaps Thasian; 500–480 B.C.
Height: 32.8 cm.; width: 23 cm.; depth (background): 4–4.5 cm.

BIBLIOGRAPHY: Cat. Sotheby April 11, 1960, no. 164 (illustrated); Hoffmann, Collecting, fig. 14.   (H. H.)

41   Head of Athena

The type is that of Athena, as identifiable by the remains of her helmet. The head is inclined forward a little and turned slightly to its left side. The face is a pointed oval and the features are soft and general: small "dreamy" eyes with the lids in relief, narrow nose, small mouth. The hair, parted in the middle, is sketchily rendered in large strands waved along the sides and joining on the nape. The ears are roughly blocked in. The top of the head was separately carved and attached with a pin, the rectangular cutting for which, measuring 8 x 10 mm., can be seen at the center of the flat sloping surface. There is evidence of drillwork in the ears and nostrils.

The head is broken at the base of the neck. The right brow is chipped and a long crack runs from the back of the head over the forehead and down the right side of her neck. Abrasions and remains of calciferous incrustation exist.

Greek; perhaps Rhodian; late Hellenistic period; marble of large crystalline structure, probably Greek islands.
Height: 15 cm.

BIBLIOGRAPHY: Hoffmann, Collecting, fig. 26 a–b.   (H. H.)

42 Fragment of Documentary Relief: Athena (Urkundenrelief)

The upper right-hand portion of a documentary stele is preserved. The marble is fine-grained yellowish, probably Pentelic. The back is roughly finished with strokes of a point; vertical at top, horizontal lower down. The marks of a toothed chisel are visible on the top edge of the stele, the corner broken away. The top of the stele is crowned by a cornice moulding consisting of a vertical upper member supported by a cymation. The surface of the relief exhibits considerable weathering; vertical solution cracks occur between Athena and the right edge of the stele. Athena is shown in effectively-rendered low relief, her body frontal, her head turned to the left. The crest of her Attic helmet overlaps the crowning moulding of the stele, increasing the three-dimensionality of the relief. She wears the belted chiton customary for her in statues and reliefs of the late fifth and fourth centuries B.C., with aegis summarily rendered by concave scallops and a tiny gorgoneion in the center. Her left arm hangs by her side; her right arm, broken off just below the shoulder, is extended toward something or someone to her left.

This fragment originally formed part of the square or rectangular relief "frontispiece" to a law, decree, treaty or other official Athenian document inscribed upon a tall, rectangular marble stele for permanent public display at some prominent spot in Athens or vicinity. These reliefs, often referred to as *Urkundenreliefs,* or documentary reliefs, generally depict allegorical subjects, often including Athena, patroness and personification of Athens; they form a uniquely valuable sequence for the dating of later classical Athenian sculpture because of the precise dates usually supplied by their inscriptions. Athena often stands beside or shakes hands with the personification of another state, as on the relief of the decree stele from 405 B.C., in the National Museum, Athens. There, Athena, standing to the right, turns toward center to clasp hands with the Samian goddess Hera, who stands to the left, in signification of the concord between the two states that results from Athens' award of privileges to Samos because of her support of Athens near the end of the Peloponnesian War. The Athena on the decree honoring Samos is generally similar to that on the Schimmel fragment. Even closer is the Athena an another relief in the National Museum, Athens, dated to 398/7 B.C. There, Athena rests her left hand against a shield that leans against her left leg. These and other examples suggest that the Schimmel fragment should be dated in the last few years of the fifth century or in the first decade of the fourth century B.C.; the absence of pilasters framing the vertical sides of the relief, a feature that becomes ubiquitous in documentary, votive and grave reliefs a few years later, likewise supports such an early date.

With further search, other fragments of the relief and inscription to which the Schimmel Athena belongs may well come to light.

Marble; Attic, ca. 405–390 B.C.
Preserved height: 28.4 cm.; preserved width: 23 cm.; width at top: 7 cm.

BIBLIOGRAPHY: For the Athenian documentary reliefs, cf. R. Binneboessel, Studien zu den attischen Urkundenreliefs des 5. und 4. Jahrhunderts (1932); B. Schweitzer, "Studien zu d. attischen Urkundenreliefs", Festgabe z. Winckelmannsfeier d. Archäol. Seminars d. Universität Leipzig (1943); for the relief of 405 B.C. honoring Samos, cf. K. Friis Johansen, Attic Grave-Reliefs of the Classical Period (Copenhagen, 1951), 150 ff.; relief of 398/7: H. K. Süsserott, Griechische Plastik des 4. Jahrhunderts v. Chr.: Untersuchungen zur Zeitbestimmung (Frankfurt-a-M., 1938; reprint Rome, "L'Erma", 1968); other parallels: J. N. Svoronos, Das Athener Nationalmuseum III (Athens, 1937), esp. nos. 427 (p. 663, pl. CCIV) and 435 (p. 665, pl. CCX, 3).   (D. G. M.)

43 Ram's Head

The fleece is rendered "impressionistically" in a series of overlapping hooked and s-shaped curls. Otherwise the modelling of the animal's head is wholly naturalistic: the carinations of the powerful horns, the eyes set under bulging brows, the long drooping muzzle with flaring nostrils and pliant nose folds. The nature of the breaks behind the preserved horn indicate that the ram was probably recumbent, with the head turned to one side, a motif recalling that of the Hellenistic bronze ram in Palermo (I. B. Marconi, Museo Nazionale Archeologico di Palermo [1969], pl. 28).

The original context of isolated lifesize animal sculptures is in most cases no longer possible to ascertain; some undoubtedly formed part of the elaborate mythological sculpture groups that decorated Roman villas and nymphaea throughout the Mediterranean (cf., for example, R. Hampe, Sperlonga and Vergil, 1972), pl. 12,2.

The greyish (Anatolian?) marble has a large crystalline structure; the surface is fire-damaged. The head is broken and mended with slight restorations in the neck area and there is some recutting on the right side of the head. The ear and nostrils were deepened with the drill.

Probably Roman, perhaps a copy or adaptation of an Early Hellenistic Greek original.

Lifesize. 24.5 cm.   (H. H.)

44   Head of a Goddess

As indicated by more completely preserved specimens from the same find, the object is undoubtedly part of a female protome, an open votive bust. Originally the composition would have included the neck and stylized shoulders.

The whole would have been painted red (the headband) and lapis blue (the earring). The diadem may have been enriched with a painted pattern. The finely modelled head conforms to the sculptural canons well documented for Eastern Greece during the Late Archaic period: "almond" eyes with both upper and lower lids strongly arched, full cheeks, lean and slightly concave nose and heavy chin. The upper and the lower lips are well differentiated; the Archaic "smile" has disappeared.

The object forms part of a *bothros* (sacred disposal pit) find of over 900 terracottas excavated by peasants near the Greek city of Knidos on the western coast of Asia Minor. Thus the goddess represented may well be Demeter, who had an important cult at Knidos. The type is generally considered to be Rhodian, but the present example may well have been produced locally, perhaps from a Rhodian mould (such as were exported as far abroad as Olbia in South Russia).

The original right edge is preserved; the other side is broken away. The head is also fractured at the top, along the diadem. It is reconstructed from five joining fragments with no restoration.

The clay is fine, non-micaceous, with some grit inclusions.

Eastern Greek; ca. 500 B.C.; said to be from the Knidian peninsula.
Height: 21 cm. (lifesize).

BIBLIOGRAPHY: H. Hoffmann, Collecting, colorplate 16. Cf. R. A. Higgins, Cat. of the Terracottas in the British Museum I (London, 1954), nos. 134–46. For the diadem and disc earrings, the standard attire of "korai", cf. G. M. A. Richter, Korai (London, 1968), 11 ff. A study of Archaic Greek terracotta protomes, by F. Croissant, is in course of preparation.   (H. H.)

44 bis   Votive Relief

The small fragment preserves the center of a well-known composition: Hades has seized Persephone and has lifted her on his chariot drawn by winged horses. With his left arm he holds the reluctant girl firmly; his right hand holds the reins. Hades wears a short chlamys and has a fillet in his hair; Persephone is clad in a peplos and has a wreath of flowers in her hair of which several tresses fall over her breasts. Both of her arms are raised in fright.

The scene is known from many different types in the series of votive reliefs form Locri. This fragment belongs to Type 57 and may join, as the owner has seen, two fragments in Palermo. In this type the scene is framed on all four sides by a slight welt; the abductor is bearded, and the movement is from left to right.

Terracotta; Locrian; 470—460 B.C.
Height: 8.0 cm.

BIBLIOGRAPHY: For the class of Locrian terracotta reliefs see Helmut Prückner, Die Lokrischen Ton-reliefs, Beiträge zur Kultgeschichte von Lokroi Epizephyrioi (Mainz, 1968), (for the type cf. pp. 68 ff.).   (D. v. B.)

45 Female Head

From the fictile revetment of the Temple of Apollo Thermios at Thermon in Aetolia, as recognized by R. Hampe. The head, part of a bust in the round, is crowned by a fillet and a polos which has been largely broken away. The face is oval, with almond eyes and slightly upturned mouth. The hair is modelled across the forehead in scalloped wavelets. The original color, of which only traces remain, can be reconstructed from better preserved duplicates (see bibliography below): the flesh was white, the hair, brows and eyes black, the cheeks and fillet red, with both red and black being used on the polos. The influence of Corinth is strong, and the somewhat softer and more provincial style of Thermon in contrast to the buoyant style of Corinth is well illustrated by this piece.

Core of pale red clay with black impurities; outer layer of fine-grained cream-colored clay; Greek; second half of the 6th century B.C.
Height: 13.7 cm.

BIBLIOGRAPHY: Metropolitan Museum Exhib. Cat., no. 173, where the head is stated to be South Italian or Sicilian. On the female head revetments from Thermon, see E. Douglas van Buren, Greek Fictile Revetments of the Archaic Period (London 1926), 64 ff., 138 ff., esp. 141, no. 12 and fig. 129, perhaps from the same mould as the Schimmel head.

(H. H.)

46 Satyr Trio

These remarkable satyrs, as suggested by Professor Hanfmann, appear to have been fashioned as illustrations of a satyr play. It is clear, at any rate, that they were created as a group in action, rather than as individually isolated figures. One runs and looks to the rear, another stands and watches, while the third tilts his head as if singing, raises his left hand, and holds his side with the right. The satyrs' bodies are handfashioned, with a minimum of attention to detail. Only their faces are pressed from moulds, and two moulds seem to have sufficed for the three figures. Despite this dearth of modelling, the expression they convey is remarkably life-like and filled with vitality. The charm of these figures is heightened by their vivid color. All three are made in the vase technique, employing intentional red glaze. That is to say, their bodies were fired orange-red while their beards and tails were deliberately turned black. Judging from their style, these satyrs would appear to have been made at the very beginning of the fifth century B.C., the period of transition from Archaic to Early Classical art. The nature of the clay and of the glaze indicate that they are Boeotian, and this would tally with their reported provenance: Megara in Boeotia.

Fine-grained brown clay; Boeotian; early 5th century B.C.
Height: (l. to r.): 11.3, 8.5, 9.9 cm.

BIBLIOGRAPHY: H. Hoffmann, Antike Kunst 7,2 (1964); G. M. A. Hanfmann, Classical Sculpture (London, 1967), 40, colorplate 5.   (H. H.)

47 Dionysos Mask

This lifesize and splendidly preserved mask belongs to a small group of terracottas assembled by W. Wrede (AM 53 [1928], 66 ff.) and shown by him to represent the wine god Dionysos. The mask is made with the help of a mould, and not individually modelled. The rear edges are trimmed off straight to form a right angle.

As indicated by four round holes – two in the headdress and two in the beard respectively – the mask was not freely suspended but fastened to a background. This background can only have been a pillar or a wall, rather than a column, and the fact that the face projects forward towards the top is an indication that the object was mounted high, above the level of the beholder. These considerations make it appear likely that the mask originally functioned either as a rural cult image – such as are known in considerable numbers from Boeotia – or as a votive offering.

The headdress has the appearance of a low spreading crown bordered at the bottom by a ring. The hair beneath is centrally parted and waved to the sides in a series of parallel strands turning abruptly upwards at the ears with the ends tucked under the crown. The eyes are relatively narrow, the nose small and lean; the lips, by contrast, are full, especially the lower lip. The god's massive spade-shaped beard is rendered in a series of long and flat parallel s-shaped curls bordered at the bottom by a second (overlapped) tier of curls with their ends rolled under. A carefully waved crescent-shaped goattee pendant from the lower lip imparts a fastidious touch. Originally the mask would have been polychrome, the bright red of the face no doubt creating an uncanny impression (cf. Pausanias VII 19, 6 ff.). The style reminds one of the heads of centaurs in the west pediment of the Temple of Zeus at Olympia. Our mask, however, is somewhat later, being closely contemporary with certain dated female terracotta protomes from Boeotia (see bibl.).

Coarse-grained yellow-ochre clay, faintly micaceous. Considerable remains of white engobe covered by traces of bright red (on the fleshy parts) and dull blue (on the beard) matt color. The iris appears to have been yellow, though this detail could not be established with certainty.

Assembled from large fragments with minor plaster restorations (parts of the r. ear, r. corner of the beard).

Greek; Boeotian, ca. 450 B.C.
Height: 30.6 cm.; thickness of the clay: ca. 1 cm.

Bibliography: L. A. Schneider, "Terrakottamaske Dionysos," AA (1972), 67 ff.   (L. A. S.)

48   Papposilenos as Teacher

The aged silen, identifiable by his bald plate, bulging forehead, snub nose and pointed ears, stands in an easy contraposto pose with his right knee slightly bent and his left foot (on a somewhat higher level) pointing outwards. His head is turned to the right and inclined upwards; his gaze is directed at his raised hand, the open palm of which is flattened (as though it once supported a now missing object, perhaps a scroll. His left hand, held at waist level, is clenched. The papposilen wears a himation, or mantle, which he has allowed to slip from the shoulder to expose his paunch and genitals.

An owner inscription in carelessly incised letters on the back of the drapery fold pendant from the arm was first noted by H. A. Cahn and read by him as MINNIOY (letter to the writer dated 10. 10. 1966). The name Minnios is Ionian (cf. L. Robert, Noms indigénes de l'Asie Mineure, 226, n. 6; ref. P. Herrmann).

Schefold published the only known replica of this intriguing statuette in his "Sokratische Wolkenverehrer" (Antike Kunst 1 [1959], 21 ff., pl. 13–15), where he interpreted the figure as greeting the clouds à la Aristophanes, 262 ff. It is important to note in this connection that whereas the raised hand of the Papposilenos published in that article (formerly coll. Dr. Schweizer, Arlesheim) has the fingers extended, the fingers of the Schimmel Papposilenos are bent. The hand of the latter cannot, therefore, be thought of as being raised in a "greeting" gesture. In my estimation Dorothy Burr Thompson (Hesperia 26 [1957], 115 ff., cited by Schefold) has offered a more convincing interpretation for the draped and dignified Papposilenos, of which she publishes several fragmentary examples. She sees in him the teacher κατ' ἐξοχήν: "The descriptions of Socrates by his contemporaries are couched in just these terms". That is, it is not the silen who (under the influence of contemporary theatre) is likened to Socrates, but vice versa: Socrates is likened to Papposilenos in accordance with an old tradition of the silen-teacher. It is this tradition which is also expressed in the known portraits of the philosopher in visual art.

The statuette is broken in several pieces and mended, with minor restorations at the back. Also restored are the toes of the right foot. The lower left arm and the thumb of the right hand are missing. The clay is damaged throughout by fire.

Fine-grained clay; said to come from Centuripe, Sicily; Hellenistic.

Height: 24 cm.   (H. H.)

49 Bird Actor

He is clad from head to foot in a feathered stage costume and strides forward with arms outstretched in the manner of wings, the left arm held slightly higher than the right. The mask which covers his head appears to be ancient and to belong. It represents the face of a wrinkled old man, shaggy-haired, bearded and with moustache, knit brows and furrowed forehead, crowned by what appears to be a pair of feathers. His feet are connected by a strut.

The fine orange-red clay is slightly micaceous. The piece was made in a front and a back mould, the latter without relief. The face under the mask is broken off.

A chorus of feathered men appear in Aristophanes' Birds: cf. T. B. L. Webster, Greek Theater Production (London 1956), 57 (F 7).

Greek, perhaps Attic or Boeotian; fourth century B.C.
Height (with mask): 18.7 cm.   (H. H.)

50 Pyxis with Lid

Lid broken and mended, with minor restorations; left-hand horse restored. The bottom is decorated with a large eight-petal rosette surrounded by a border of diagonally striped leaves, parallel lines and running scrolls. The decoration of the body is divided into metopes and triglyphs, the metopes containing alternatively a striped swastika and a striped quatrofoil ornament, the latter having four triangular grids in the interstices. The lid is decorated with tongue pattern, concentric lines, running scrolls and broad bands. The two horses that stand in the center and serve as handles are covered with glaze but for their heads and a panel on their chests containing zigzag decoration. Their eyes and bridles are indicated by means of glaze-lines.

Terracotta; Attic Geometric; middle of the 8th century B.C.
Height (max.): 22.5 cm.; diameter (max.): 32.5 cm.

BIBLIOGRAPHY: J. Fink, Archäologischer Anzeiger 1966, 483 ff. and figs.   (H. H.)

50 bis   Aryballos (or lekythos)

Broken and repaired, but virtually complete (a small triangular sliver on the shoulder is missing and has been restored). The glaze has flaked in places and, in general, has not fired uniformly.

The top portion of the vase is shaped in the form of an owl's head. The conceit of an owl is continued on the shoulders which are decorated with the wings of an owl and the plumage of its chest. Below the shoulders the scheme of decoration follows the convention of contemporary aryballoi (sometimes also called lekythoi): a main frieze is given over to two heraldic sphinxes (on the obverse) and two heraldic lions (on the reverse). Above, below, and between the figures ten star-rosettes are placed symmetrically. The narrow frieze below consists of four hounds running to right. Above the ring base, twenty-two rays. Added red is used for circles in the eyes of the owl, dots on its head and neck, alternating flight feathers of the wings; hair and wingbars of the sphinxes and a stripe on the haunches; mane and tongues of the lions, three stripes on the flanks and a stripe on the haunches. The friezes are bordered above and below by three lines.

The orifice on the back of the owl's head is decorated with a circular wave-pattern. The flat strap handle has a cable-pattern on top and a step-pattern on the edge. The aryballos invites comparison with the lion-headed aryballos London 89.4–18.1 (the 'Macmillan' aryballos: Payne, Protokorinthische Vasenmalerei [Berlin 1933], pl. 22, 1, 2, 5) save that it is almost twice as big. The sculptured parts of the aryballos, on the other hand, and the convention of painting eyes, beak and wings are very close to the plastic owl in the Louvre (CA 1737: Payne, op. cit., pl. 25, 1–2). Both must be contemporary and if not by the same hand, at least from the same workshop. The Louvre owl is a complete bird, but on the Schimmel vase the traditional profile of a standard lekythos harmonizes with the contours of an owl, and the ingenious combination of lekythos and sculptural adjuncts produce the overall effect of an owl, whereas the lion-headed aryballos in London does not give the illusion of a complete lion.

The shaping of the head is technically interesting. It was thrown on the wheel together with the body and while still soft pinched into the face of an owl. The opening on top was then closed by adding clay and twisting it. The mouth and handle were then added and the proper orifice was punched in with a stick.

Proto-Corinthian, developed polychrome style. Mid-seventh century B.C.
Height: 12.39 cm.; diameter: 7.44 cm.; diameter of base: 3.12 cm.   (D. v. B.)

51 Aryballos

A fragment of the rim is missing. Cavalcade of three horsemen to right. One the bottom, a large whirl within two circles. Warrior Group (cf. Payne, Necrocorinthia, 228 f, pl. 21, 10).

Early Corinthian; last quarter of the 7th century B.C.
Height: 6.6 cm.

BIBLIOGRAPHY: "Le dessin dans l'art grec", catalogue of an exhibition held at the Maspero Gallery, Paris, April–June 1963, no. 2.   (H. H.)

52 Aryballos

Komast with drinking horn to right between two facing horsemen; under the handle, a siren with spread wings and wearing a polos faces right. On the bottom, a large rosette framed by a dot-band between two lines. By the same hand as the preceding.

Early Corinthian; last quarter of the 7th century B.C.
Height: 7.2 cm.   (H. H.)

53 Tripod "Kothon"

The bowl-shaped body with in-turned rim is supported by three rail-like legs. These vases were most probably scent containers; their construction is such as to make accidental spilling practically impossible. The decoration is in black glaze with added

red. On the body are three animal pairs: two confronting grazing dams, their ears overlapping; two panthers flanking an upright palmette (their tails enclose a drop shape); two sphinxes flanking an upright bud shape on a stem. An incised rosette, a dot rosette and crosses are in the field. Above (on the rim) is a zone of squiggles and a zone of rays separated by two lines; below is a row of blobs between two lines. The pictures on the legs have horizontal frames topped by a row of dots between two lines and bordered below by a reserved band and a glazed flange. 1) boxers at a tripod (three crosses in the field; 2) two dancing komasts (two crosses in the field); 3) two standing komasts, one holding a kantharos, the other drinking from an oinochoe (in the field, a dot rosette and seven crosses). The underneath of the bowl and the sides of the legs are black; the back of the legs and a ring at the center of the bottom are reserved. Red: faces, necks and shoulders of the sphinxes, necks of dams, necks, noses and foreheads of panthers, core of palmette, faces and necks of boxers and komasts.

For the function of these objects cf. R.M. Burrows, P.N. Ure, JHS 31 (1911), 72 ff., fig. 12. The lid is missing and minor repainting occurs on the legs. One leg is broken and mended; the glaze is crackled.

Terracotta; Boetian; ca. 570 B.C. Possibly by the same hand as the tripod kothon, Athens NM 12924, Burrows, Ure, op. cit., fig. 12. Cf. also an Attic example, Beazley, ARV.² 41, 27.
Height: 13.6 cm; diameter: 18.4 cm. (H. H.)

54 Pointed Lekythos

Two confronting sphinxes, a large water bird between them, are figured in the principal zone. Behind them there is a bull to the right. The empty spaces contain carefully drawn dot-rosettes, and these are also contained in the subsidiary frieze, in which two running hounds and a sitting hare are shown. Below, eight rays; on the bottom, a dot within a circle. The top of the mouth is decorated with a register of dots surrounded by a register of rays. On the rim there is a dot band, on the handle a ladder of thirteen rungs. The shoulder is ornamented with alternate red and black tongues, and red is employed also for the faces and breasts of the sphinxes, as well as their wing bars and alternate feathers of the wings, the bull's neck, the hounds' necks, and the hare's stomach.

Pale yellow clay; transitional Corinthian; ca. 630 B.C.
Height: 7.6 cm; diameter of rim: 3.3 cm; diameter of foot: 1 cm.

BIBLIOGRAPHY: Compare CVA. Copenhagen 2, pl. 86, 1 (=Pfuhl, Malerei und Zeichnung, III, fig. 82) and H. Bloesch, Antike Kleinkunst in Winterthur, similar but by different hands.

(H.H.)

55   Black-figured Band-Cup

Broken and mended, with part of one handle restored. The inside is black (misfired to brown), with the exception of a reserved circle in the center which contains two concentric circles in black glaze. The handle zones picture a cockfight with hens watching and a swan with raised wings between two lions.

Red and white accessory colors. Palmettes on long stems flank the handles.

Near the Tleson Painter. Cf. ABV, 179 ff., esp. 180, no. 42.

Attic; ca. 550 B.C.
Height: 10.2 cm.; diameter (without handles): 14.6 cm.

BIBLIOGRAPHY: Beazley, Paralipomena, 76.   (H. H.)

56   Cup by the Amasis Painter

Cup of shape A, with deep bowl and flaring stem separated by a fillet.
Broken and mended, with the restorations visible in the photographs.
Broken and restored also in antiquity. Side A: harnessing scene. Four
grooms with four tethered horses (of a quadriga). The right-hand
groom, who holds a goad, reaches for a harness strap which hangs
from the abacus of the column next to him. To the left, the three other
grooms, two naked, the third wearing a patterned kilt, are engaged in
calming their horses, which rear and toss their manes nervously (as
frequently in scenes of harnessing; cf., for example, the amphora,
Boston 89.275, ABV. 144, 4, by Exekias). At the right end, a bearded
man, wrapped in a dotted himation and holding a spear or staff, observes the proceedings.

The horses' nervousness is apparently occasioned by the mysterious proceedings around them. Unnoted by the grooms an archer on a smaller scale has lept onto the back of the far-left horse and is about to release an arrow in the direction of the groom in front of him. Behind him a second small figure, naked, seems to leap from one horse to the other, grasping the abacus of the column in front of him in order to steady himself. It has been suggested that he is scaling the column for a better view (by H. Jucker, cited below).

We return to the architectural setting of this curious scene. Usually in stable representations on Greek vases, only the columns to which the horses are tethered, and occasionally the beam above, are shown. Here, cushioned by an intermediary block (having no corresponding member in any known example of Greek architecture), the column capitals support an elaborate frieze of twenty-six metopes – fourteen miniature pictures and twelve empty frames. The pictures, from left to right, include four birds (probably partridges), a squatting monkey, a panther, another bird, a monkey bending over in a characteristic position, a swan with spread wings, a lion (?), a bird, a dog (?), a monkey in the act of climbing out of his metope (!) and, in the last frame, a crouching archer who appears to be taking aim at the retreating monkey.

The mysterious archer on the horse's back may be a demon (Taraxippos has been suggested, on the analogy of the Corinthian pinax in Berlin, cf. Roscher, ML, s.v. "Taraxippos", fig. 1, which, however, shows the mischief maker as a phallic imp). He and his companion (?) do not appear to be acrobats (cf. the black-figured amphora from Camiros, Gardner, Athletics, fig. 205). Nor do I find Jucker's suggestion of an intruding Greek or Trojan persuasive (cf. H. Jucker, in Studia Oliveriana 13–14 [1966], note 132). It is difficult to decide whether the scene reflects myth or depicts an "ordinary" stable scene. Jucker (loc. cit.) points to Iliad 13, 21 ff., the stable of Poseidon where the god is seen prior to his departure for the Trojan War (his arrival on the battlefield is shown on side B of the Schimmel cup, described below); he also calls attention to the Amasis Painter's Leningrad amphora (Beazley, ABV 151, 15; Jucker, op. cit. 41, note 41), where rearing horses are shown in the context of a harnessing scene (a subsequent phase of the scene on the Schimmel cup?).

Side B. Poseidon between the two Ajaxes, summoning them and their companions to battle (Iliad 13, 125 ff.). (Interpretation by H. Jucker, op. cit. note 132, and M. Milne independently). Ajax, the son of Telamon, to right of Poseidon, wears a Corinthian helmet and greaves and carries a spear and a shield beautifully emblazoned with a ram (compare the Amasis Painter's Boston amphora, ABV. 152, 26).

Ajax, the son of Oileos, wears a Corinthian helmet, corslet, chitoniskos and greaves and carries shield and spear. Poseidon appears between them striding energetically from right to left and turning his head to look round. The god, clad in chiton and chlamys and carrying his trident, raises his hand in greeting. To the left of the main group comes an archer, holding bow and battle-axe and wearing his quiver from the waist. His dress is unusual: patterned stockings that cover the calves only, not unlike Bavarian "Stutzen", in addition to the customary skin-tight archer's garment and stocking-cap. Behind him

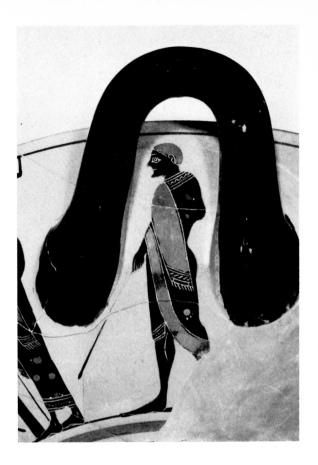

stands a draped youth with spear, a bystander. To the right of center, another archer holds his bow in one hand and an arrow in the other and turns to converse with his helmeted neighbor. The latter wears a fringed chiton over a chitoniskos, carries a spear, has a sword suspended by a baldric at his side, but is without greaves and shield-less. Of the next warrior, only the lower half is preserved: greaved legs, part of a shield emblazoned with a lion-protome (one of the Amasis Painter's favorite devices, cf. Antike Kunst 3, 1960, 76) and a spear. Then comes the usual bystander, another draped youth with spear.

There is a solitary figure under each handle (see details): the bearded youth with stick faces and belongs to the equine scene; the helmeted warrior with spear is a straggler from the meeting of warriors.

This is richest and, together with the Boston siren cup, most unusual work by the Amasis Painter known to date. The shape of the cup, type A (only one other cup type A by the Amasis Painter has come down to us: Mainz inv. 88, CVA. I pl. 41), and the advanced and daring style of the drawing indicate that it belongs to the later phase of the Amasis Painter's career. The date will be about 540 B.C.

Said to be from Vulci; by the Amasis Painter; Attic black-figure; ca. 540 B.C.
Height: 12.4 cm.; diameters: (bowl) 25.7 cm., (handles) 33 cm., (foot) 12.2 cm.

BIBLIOGRAPHY: Beazley, Paralipomena, 67; K. Schauenburg, JDI 79 (1964), 112, note 8 (with the unsupported claim that the Schimmel cup is not by the Amasis Painter).   (H. H.)

57 Red-figured Psykter with Dolphin Riders by Oltos

Broken and mended, with part of one dolphin's body and the edge of its rider's shield (the one with cup emblem) restored; a small part of the vessel's neck and most of the foot are also restoration.

A procession of six leaping dolphins encircles the body of the psykter, and each carries a fully armed hoplite on its back. When the psykter, a cooling vessel, was filled with wine and bobbing up and down in a large container of ice-cold water, the dolphins would appear to swim on the surface of the liquid – or rather, to leap from its depths and submerge again.

The six hoplites resemble one another closely. Each wears a cuirass over a short chiton, a Corinthian helmet and greaves, and each is armed with shield and spear. Even their postures on the dolphins and the way they hold their weapons are almost identical, as befitting a well-disciplined military squadron. The individuality of the figures reposes entirely in the emblems painted on their shields. The artist has selected and arranged these carefully, so as to impart a certain rhythm to the scene. There are three vessels and three "zoological" representations, and these follow each other in an alternating sequence. The vessels – a krater, a kantharos and a cup – are carefully observed and closely resemble actual vessels of the period. Thus, for example, the slender volute krater reminds one greatly of the Berlin Painter's krater of similar shape in the Villa Giulia, and the shape of the cup is rendered accurately enough to permit one to attribute the model to a particular group of large black-figured band-cups assembled by Beazley (ABV., 265).

The alternate shield devices are whirls of three different types. The

first connects four dolphins to the spokes of a wheel, a very unusual juxtaposition (although single dolphins as shield emblems are by no means uncommon in Attic vase-painting). Then comes a triskelis; three running legs, the symbol of human industry. The final and most elaborate of these devices combines the foreparts of a lion, a horse, and a griffin – each with forelegs and wings.

Each dolphin rider is accompanied by the same retrograde inscription; ΕΠΙΔΕΛΦΙΝΟΣ ("upon the dolphin"). These inscriptions appear to be of significance to the proper understanding of the curious scene depicted, for surely they convey something more than merely an explanation of the obvious.

F. Brommer collected a number of representations of dolphin riders some thirty years ago. He interpreted them in the light of Greek theatrical performances – for the dolphin riders he assembled (among them those on the celebrated skyphos in Boston) are without exception accompanied by a flute player. The similarity of the dolphin riders represented on our psykter with these "choruses" of dolphin riders is so obvious that, despite the fact that there is no flute player on the psykter, one would hardly wish to disassociate them from the stage context of Brommer's group. It might be pointed out, moreover, that all the vases representing dolphin riders are approximately contemporary, an indication that they may reflect a specific work performed at this time on the Athenian stage.

If we translate *epidelphinos* as "dolphin rider" (rather than the more literal "upon the dolphin") – and if indeed there were a theatrical production featuring dolphin riders being performed on the Athenian stage of the later sixth century – the inscriptions may conceivably furnish us the title of the play: EPIDELPHINOS. G. M. Sifakis has interpreted the inscriptions as the words of the rider's song, rhythms which fit very well for a choral entry (anapaestic dimeters).

The painter of our psykter was first recognized by D. von Bothmer when the piece was on the Geneva art market. It is a work by Oltos, one of the earliest red-figure vase-painters. The painter's best works – including a psykter in the Metropolitan Museum – date late in his career, during the decade 520–510 B.C. It is doubtless at this time that our psykter was created.

Attributed to Oltos; Attic red-figure; ca. 520–510 B.C.
Height, as restored: 30.2 cm.; diameter: 22.7 cm.

BIBLIOGRAPHY: Beazley, ARV.², 1622 f.; A. Greifenhagen, Pantheon 23 (1965) 1 ff.; Beazley, Paralipomena, 259, 326. Mentioned in Jahrbuch der Berliner Museen 2 (1961) 123, note 11 (Greifenhagen). A list of psykters is given by Caskey-Beazley, Attic Vase-paintings in the Museum of Fine Arts, Boston, II (1951) 3 ff. G. M. Sifakis, "Singing Dolphin Riders," Institute of Classical Studies, University of London Bulletin, 14 (1967), 36–7 pl. VI. A. D. Trendall and T. B. L. Webster, Illustrations of Greek Drama, (London, 1971), I, 15.　　　(A. G.)

58   Stand

The stand is broken and repaired with two small triangular areas restored. The stem and foot are missing and restored on the analogy of another similar stand in the Metropolitan Museum.

On each side there is a sphinx. This very rare vase is one of a pair that to date represents the only Attic counterpart to a well-known Etruscan shape. Its construction is quite complex. The potter made a cylinder on the wheel and slit the tube lengthwise. He, or a coroplast, next added the projections by hand and stamped the moulding along the edges. A foot and stem were likewise made on the wheel and joined to the half cylinder in the middle of its wall. The painter then added the painted decoration for which he employed several techniques: red-figure for the body, the incision of black-figure for the wing coverts, and outline for the primaries. White was added, according to black-figure convention, to the human flesh of the sphinxes, both on the plastic parts (their faces and necks) and on the two-dimensional chests. The edges of the wheelmade portion are slightly bevelled and decorated with an ivy wreath in black silhouette, while the edges of the wings are painted red. Some of the primary feathers are also painted red. In the feline portion of the sphinxes there are no inner markings, and the relief line has been used sparingly.

The stand cannot be considered without referring to its more complete counterpart in the Metropolitan Museum of Art, and both have been fully published side by side in Revue Archéologique 1972, pp. 84–85. The conclusions there reached may therefore be summarized. For the shape we have to go outside Attica and look at the impressive series of Etruscan stands of this shape, which were made in bucchero and develop from simple troughs to elaborate structures that include sculptural adjuncts. There also is a fragmentary Etruscan stand that has decoration painted in black-figure while retaining sculptural adjuncts first introduced in bucchero. The two red-figured stands are obviously Attic and may be taken as fanciful elaborations of a rather inelegant Etruscan prototype. Nothing is known of their function, although some theories have been advanced. The frequency of the shape in bucchero connects it with shapes desired for tomb furnishings.

Stylistically the two red-figured stands are related to the potter Sikanos and the Euergides Painter. The technique points to a very early period in Attic red-figure, about 520 B.C.

Height, as restored: 26.2 cm.; as preserved: 15.45 cm.; wing spread on A: 16.76 cm.; on B: 16.6 cm.; distance of wings A–B: 17.5–17.74 cm.

BIBLIOGRAPHY: Alluded to by H. Hoffmann und Patricia F. Davidson, Greek Gold (1965), 290–291 summary description of the pair and unverified provenance); AJA 70 (1966) p. 184; Hoffmann, Collecting, color plate 13; D. von Bothmer "A Unique Pair of Attic Vases," Revue Archéologique (1972), 83–92.

(D. v. B.)

Broken and mended in antiquity; broken afresh and repaired. The surface is pitted in places; the underside of the foot is curiously scratched. Complete except for a rim fragment with the upper part of the body of the second athlete on one side of the exterior. Frames: inside, simple line border; outside, two lines spaced relatively far apart.

The tondo shows a woman with both hands submerged in a shallow laver. In front of her feet stands a bucket; the notched bail is upright. Behind her a small wine-skin is suspended, and above the laver, hugging the circle of the frame, a skyphos. The woman wears a pleated chiton, the overfold tied around her waist, and an elaborate sakkos. The laver has a fluted shaft surmounted by an abacus; its offset rim is decorated with a kymation moulding. The action of the woman is not very clear, and the wine-skin and skyphos seem to be out of place in the context of an ablution. In the field, the inscriptions ΗΟ ΠΑΙΣ ΚΑΛΟΣ (the last word retrograde) and ΚΑΟΕ (apparently meaningless).

The subject of the exterior is eight boy athletes, divided evenly between the two sides. On A, a boy has picked up two acontia and faces another boy who probably held a diskos. Between them appears a stubby column or post. A sponge, strigil and aryballos suspended from the wall separate this group from the next: a jumper with jumping weights and a boy readying to throw the javelin. Between the two heads, again suspended from the wall, hang another sponge, aryballos and strigil. Between the legs of the acontist appears a pick with one end buried in the ground. On B, the first boy picks up a diskos; he faces a boy about to throw the javelin. The right half consists of another jumper facing a boy with two javelins. A pick is partly buried in the ground, and between the four athletes are three suspended aryballoi, the first two accompanied by strigils. On A and B are traces of ΗΟ ΠΑΙΣ ΚΑΛΟΣ.

The subject of the tondo bears some resemblance to the tondo of the namepiece of the Thorvaldsen Group (Beazley ARV² p. 455, no. 2), a group which is near the Magnoncourt Painter and the earliest Douris, but the drawing of the Schimmel cup is finer and must be by Douris himself. In his earliest period the anatomical marking of athletes is still somewhat tentative and while the lines are all there, the perspective is not yet fully mastered which affects less the contours of the bodies than their component parts. Thus the chest is relatively small with the nipples set right on the line of the pectoral muscle, and the clavicles do not terminate properly.

The use of buckets in filling lavers is best illustrated by the cup attributed to Onesimos in the Louvre (G 291; Beazley ARV² p. 322, no. 36 and p. 1706). The notch in the handle, so clearly shown on the Douris cup, is surely a device to keep the rope from slipping.

The potting may be by Euphronios, as are others among the earliest cups attributed to Douris (Beazley ARV² pp. 427–428, nos. 1, 2, and 13).

By Douris, about 500 B.C.
Height: 11.2 cm.; width: 34.6 cm.; diameter: 26.76–26.85 cm.; diameter of foot: 10.67 cm.; diameter of tondo: 15.5 cm.   (D. v. B.)

Outside of Cup by Douris, No. 59

60 Cup by Onesimos

Broken and mended, with two fragments of the rim restored. Decorated in the interior only. Within a meander medallion, a Negro groom wearing a fillet in his hair stands beside a tethered horse which lifts a front and a rear hoof impatiently and seems to be neighing. He places his right hand on the horse's back and gazes at a rectangular object in the upturned palm of his left. R. Hampe explained the exact meaning of this representation to me: The groom, having finished currying the horse, is now sighting along his curry-comb for hairs, the final stage of the grooming. A whisk-broom hangs from the wall. Inscribed: "Lykos is fair". Red accessory color for the groom's fillet, the tether and the inscription.

Attributed by Beazley to Onesimos; Attic red-figure ca. 480 B.C.
Height: 9 cm.; diameter (max.): 31.1 cm.

BIBLIOGRAPHY: ARV.², 329, no. 125 bis (Onesimos); Katalog der II. Auktion der Ars Antiqua A.G., Lucerne, 13 May 1960, no. 153, pl. 16 (K. Schauenburg); F. Eckstein, Deutsche Literaturzeitung 87,6 (June 1966), 526; Beazley, Paralipomena, 359; N. Himmelmann, Archäologisches zum Problem der griechischen Sklaverei (1972), 19, fig. 16. For the name Lykos, see ARV.², 1595 f.   (H.H.)

61   Cup by the Antiphon Painter

Broken and mended, with minor restorations and repaints. These include the right pelvic area of the youth in the interior, parts of the krater (including the left handle) and its platform and the right foot of the youth dipping from the krater. The flaked relief lines of the vomiting man's head and thoracic area have been reinforced with India ink. Chipped and flaked in places.

Inside, within a meander medallion, a youthful komast wearing chlamys and boots appears to be doing a slow dance step, lifting his chlamys with one hand and extending his staff behind him at arm's length with the other. An empty flute case hanging from the wall indicates that the setting is indoors. Around the periphery of the medallion, the faded love-inscription: "Aristarchos is fair". The name occurs on the Antiphon Painter's cup in Baltimore (Beazley, ARV.², 336, no. 16 and 1566).

Outside, on both sides, a komos of men and youths. On one side, a youth with boots turned down plays a kithara in front of a krater (inscribed: καλός) into which a second youth holding a skyphos is about to dip an oinochoe. To the left, a bearded reveler holding a skyphos moves away. An amusing touch is his staff, which seems to lean against the handle of the cup. An empty flute case hangs from the wall, as on the interior. On the other side, a bearded man leaning on his staff clasps his head as he vomits. A naked boy carrying a staff and a basket, perhaps his servant, urges him to hurry up. Above his staff, the inscription: καλός.

To the right, a second bearded man, who also has overimbibed, makes his way precariously forward, extending his foot gingerly and supporting himself with this staff. He holds out a skyphos, and a youth rushes up to fill it, spilling wine on the ground in his haste. The bearded man's words are τέλος = "the end", referring perhaps, to his empty cup. Red accessory color for the wreaths, wine drippings, vomit, plektron, basket cord and inscriptions (except the one on the krater, which is black). Muscles are rendered with great delicacy in dilute glaze.

Said to be from Vulci. By the Antiphon Painter (attribution kindly confirmed by Beazley).
Attic red-figure; ca. 490–480 B.C.
Height: 12.7 cm.; diameter (max.): 39.7 cm.

For the painter, whose style derives from, and runs parallel to the later style of Onesimos (see no. 60), see ARV.², 335 ff.

BIBLIOGRAPHY: Beazley, Paralipomena, 362.   (H. H.)

62   Lekythos by the Pan Painter

Broken and repaired with much flaking. Half of the handle restored in plaster. The floral decoration on the shoulder is in red-figure. It consists of a kymation and a hanging nine-fronded palmette to which are joined, with tendrils and volutes, two upright seven-fronded palmettes and two buds lying on their sides. The picture field on most of the cylinder is on a white ground that is worn, abraded, or restored in places. It is bordered above by a continuous band of stopt maeanders to right, interrupted every two maeanders by a saltire square. The picture represents a girl or woman clad in a chiton and a himation who transfers balls of wool from a kalathos to a cloth bag. Her right foot is shown frontally, her left foot is done in profile, as are her breasts, neck and head. In her hair she wears a diadem. In the field, diagonally above the wool basket, HE ΠΑΙΣ and above her left arm K]AΛE. Below the cloth bag stands a diphros (cf. Miss Richter's type 4: The Furniture of the Greeks, Etruscans and Romans [London 1966] p. 42) with a cushion that is decorated with little crosses. If the hanging palmette on the shoulder is to be taken as the central meridian, the figure is mostly to right of center.

Black glaze is employed for the ornamental band above, the hair of the girl, her eye, details of the wicker basket, the stool, and the inscriptions. All other contours and some of the details are painted in dilute glaze. The himation is painted in deep vermillion with some of the folds indicated in a darker hue. The diadem in her hair is purple with a white line. Her flesh, her chiton, the balls of wool and the bag are painted in "second white" which has fired an off-color and does not contrast greatly with the white of the engobe. In technique and subject matter this lekythos goes with one in Syracuse (19900; ARV² p. 557, no. 122; first mentioned by Petersen RM 7 [1892] p. 182 and by Orsi in ML 17 [1906] cols. 364–365, note 1). Here similar balls of wool are twisted into a rope of nine strands; the balls are black. Another white lekythos by the Pan Painter is in Leningrad (670; ARV² p. 557, no. 121); it is close to the new one in height (37.7 cm.) and in the use of second white. Here, too, the engobe is off-white. In the caption to the first illustration of Mr. Schimmel's vase (Philipp von Zabern, Archaeological Calendar 1971, Oct., 1971) Erika Simon explained the action as filling a pillow slip with balls of wool, but her reconstruction of the scene was based on a misleading restoration of the bag which has since been removed.

Attributed by Beazley to the Pan Painter, about 470 B.C.
Height: 37.1 cm.; diameter of shoulder: 13.04 cm.; diameter of mouth: 6.9 cm. (the foot is too restored to permit a precise measurement).

BIBLIOGRAPHY: Philipp von Zabern, Archaeological Calendar 1971, October, 1971.

(D. v. B.)

63   Lekythos by the Achilles Painter

Unbroken, save for the false bottom which has become detached from the inside of the neck and has fallen into the vase. White ground on shoulder and most of the cylinder. Vent-hole in black portion on the meridian of the handle. At the junction of neck and shoulder, kymation. On the shoulder, hanging palmette connected with tendrils to two upright palmettes. Each has five fronds painted in thinned glaze that alternate with six fronds painted in matte red, now mostly faded or rubbed off. The figure zone is bordered above by an ornamental band of stopt maeanders going, alternately, from left to right and from right to left. The maeanders are interrupted after every third (or, once, every fourth) unit by squares filled with saltire crosses. The glaze lines framing the pattern run all the way round the vase, while the pattern itself does not go much beyond the space occupied by the figures.

On the body, a tall youth shown in profile, clad in a dark red himation approaches a funerary stele: his right arm is held in a gesture of prayer. On the other side of the stele is shown a smaller boy, his left leg and body frontal, his head in profile to left. He wears a vermillion himation. His extended right arm touches the shaft of the stele. Over his head hovers his soul, a small stick-figure painted in silhouette in profile to left. The soul has wings; one arm is bent and touches his head; the other is extended downward. The tomb monument has a small pediment with three acroteria and two ornamental horizontal bands below. Red stripes border the slope of the pediment and the kymation below; a red and a black fillet are tied to the shaft of the stele; a second red fillet hangs from the top step; another fillet painted in glaze hangs from the top of the bottom step. Against its vertical face is painted a second glaze fillet rounded into a wreath. The anatomical markings and the hair are painted in glaze, at times thinned.

Of the hundred-odd white lekythoi attributed to the Achilles Painter by far the largest proportion show only women — either two of equal rank that may be related, or a mistress and a maid. One quarter of all his white lekythoi have a woman with a warrior, a man, a youth, or a boy. Only three in addition to the one here published show a youth and a boy, and among those three, the lekythos now in Aachen (ARV² p. 999, no. 171) is particularly close in composition and mood. Rare, too, is the pediment with acroteria that surmounts the shaft of the stele, and, for that matter, the presence of a tomb is in itself a relative rarity. But the most unusual feature on this lekythos is surely the image of the soul that appears directly above the head of the boy and thus denotes him as the one who has died. Other souls on lekythoi are normally in flight and appear to be fluttering about Charon's bark, the bier, or the tomb (cf. ARV² pp. 999–1000, nos. 177 and 193). This feature, coupled with the exceptionally fine preservation and the sure execution of line and coloring, raises this lekythos to the highest level of the acknowledged masterpieces by the Achilles Painter.

By the Achilles Painter, about 440 B.C.
Height: 37.4–36.8 cm. (the neck is warped); diameter of shoulder: 11.78 cm.; diameter of mouth: 6.88 cm.; diameter of foot: 8.15 cm; height of figure zone exclusive of border: 15.8 cm.   (D. v. B.)

 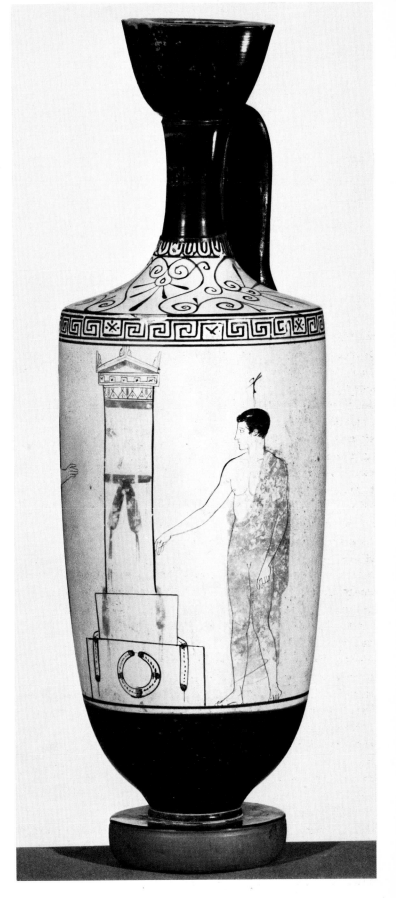

64 Bowl

The bowl has a foot, two upright handles with knobs, and offset rim. Broken and repaired with hardly anything missing. Some of the added color has flaked off.

The small tondo of the bowl shows a dolphin swimming above a sea-perch. The tondo is surrounded by a zone framed above by a kymation and below by a wave pattern. In the zone are a crampfish (torpedo), another perch, a dog fish, a gray mullet, and a triton's trumpet. The perch is drawn upside down, and the dog fish is rendered in top view. This zone is, in turn, surrounded by a wreath of vines.

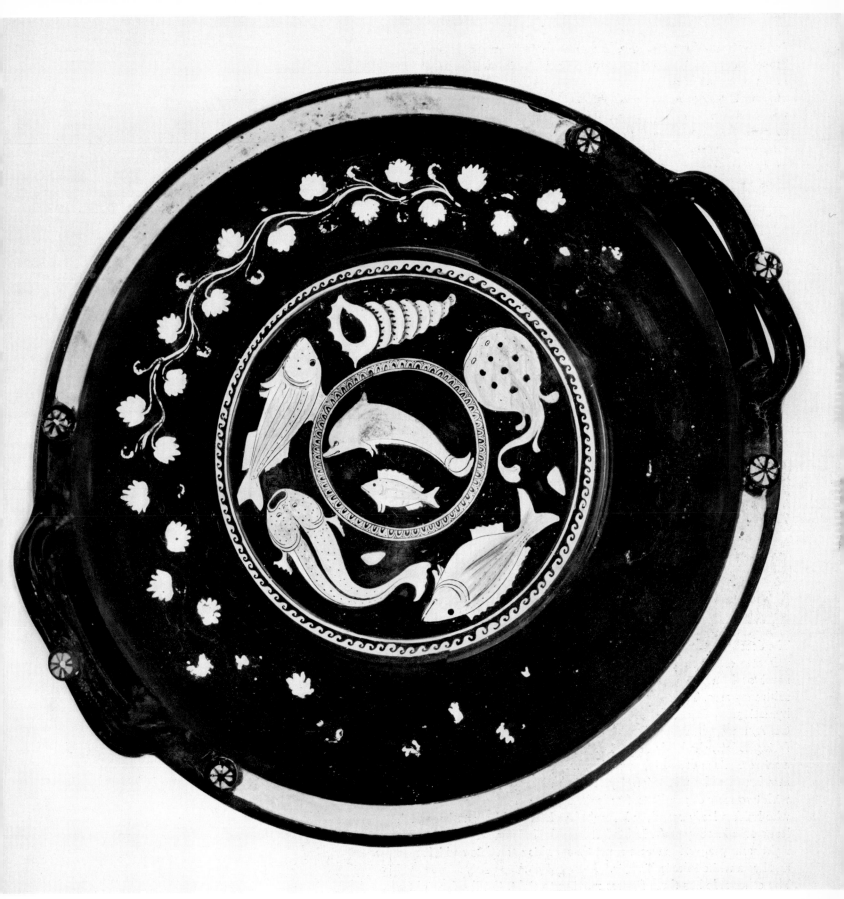

The decoration on the outside is divided in two halves by an elaborate palmette configuration below each handle; it is framed below by a band of leftward maeanders interrupted at irregular intervals by saltire squares. The side of the overhanging rim is decorated with a kymation.

On A, a woman or goddess leans on a pillar. Her legs are crossed; facing to left, she holds in her left hand a tympanon and in her right a mirror. She is dressed in a peplos, wears shoes, and her hair is tied in a broad ribbon. Her jewelry consists of bracelets and a necklace with two rows of pendants. She looks at a youth seated on his mantle who holds a leafy branch in his right hand. Behind her another youth leans on a knobby staff. In his left hand he holds a strigil and in his right some grapes. He wears a mantle over his shoulders and left arm and has a white fillet in his hair.

The other side has three figures moving to right. On the far right a

woman carries a cylindrical basket and grapes, followed by a youth with a torch and another woman who holds a tympanon and a laurel branch. The youth wears a mantle over his left arm; the women wear peploi, shoes, and decorated hair-bands. Both have necklaces, bracelets, and earrings. Here, as on the obverse, there are filling ornaments.

Apulian red-figure. The bowl has been attributed by Trendall to the Painter of Naples Stg. 366 who belongs to the Group of Taranto 8893 which in turn is connected with New York 28.57.10. All of these are closely connected in style with the Darius Painter, moving towards the Underworld Painter.

About 340–330 B.C.

Height: 20.5 cm.; diameter: 48.5 cm.; width: 53.0 cm.

BIBLIOGRAPHY: H. Hoffmann, Collecting, 134, figs. 110 a–b. (D. v. B.)

65   Fish Plate

Three sea-perch are disposed around the central depression, which is decorated with a rosette and surrounded by wave pattern. Wave pattern also on the rim.

Formerly in the H. Kevorkian Collection; last third of the 4th century B.C.
Height: 7.6 cm.; diameter: 22.3 cm.

BIBLIOGRAPHY: Parke-Bernet Sale 14 December, 1962 (Kevorkian Collection), no. 233. Cf. Notizie degli Scavi 12 (1936), 357 ff. (for the date).   (H.H.)

65 bis   Stemmed Askos

This elaborate vessel is furnished with a pouring spout in the shape of a bird's head and a columnar spout for filling. It also has a bail handle for easy lifting. The principal decoration on the sides of the askos proper is set in panels. The chief picture on one side is a hunter facing a stag. Four other panels have water birds. The remaining decoration is ornamental.

Italo-Geometric (Bisenzio Class), early seventh century B.C.
Height: 33.5 cm.; length: 42.3 cm.

BIBLIOGRAPHY: For the class of vases to which this askos belongs see Åke Åkerström, Der geometrische Stil in Italien (Uppsala, 1943), p. 64 and pl. 13, 1—2; the askos was acquired together with a stemmed barrel vase of the type Åkerström, op. cit., pl. 12,4.   (D. v. B)

66   Black-figured Skyphos

Decorated on each side with a pair of facing satyrs who step forward energetically, as if dancing, and raise a clenched fist. They hold their own tails with the other hand. The vigorous sketchy drawing resembles the work of the Siren Painter.

Said to be from Vulci; Etruscan; ca. 520 B.C.
Height: 7.7 cm.

BIBLIOGRAPHY: Worcester Cat. no. 32. On the Siren Painter, see T. Dohrn, Die etruskisch-schwarzfigurigen Vasen (Berlin, 1937), 89 ff., 151 ff. Cf. the amphora Baltimore 48.7, D. K. Hill, Journal of the Walters Art Gallery 3 (1940), 111 ff., 137, no. 3, fig. 1.   (H. H.)

67   Plastic Vase in the Shape of a Kneeling Horse

Covered with brown incrustation. The animal kneels on tubular forelegs. The body – barrel-shaped and devoid of all anatomical detail – forms a curious contrast to the beautifully modelled head and neck graced by an elegantly clipped mane and heart-shaped forelock. The hind legs are rudimentary stumps; the tail is made of the same stuff as the forelegs and forms a projecting loop. A lekythos mouth, for filling, flanked by ribbon handles, are set on the horse's back, and a tapering spout is mounted at an angle on the rump.

A number of such curious animal vessels have come to light in the area of Selinunte and seem to have been locally produced (cf. Auktion XXII der Münzen und Medaillen A.G., Basel, 13. Mai 1961, nos. 186 and 187, with bibliography). They often are decorated with sketchily drawn figures, similar to those found on the pottery from the Theban Cabeirion.

Terracotta; Sicilian, probably Selinunte; 5th century B.C.
Height: 13.5 cm.; length: 17 cm.

BIBLIOGRAPHY: Cf. AA, 1964, 785, n. 110, figs. 89–90 (from the Manicalunge necropolis near Selinunte; ref. F. Eckstein).   (H. H.)

68 Foot Guttus

This vase is in the form of a right foot wearing a sandal. It is mould-made in right and left median halves, with the sole applied as a flat slab of clay. A strainer mouth with six small perforations has been added separately, as have a small lion-mask spout at the back and a bipartite ring handle. The sole and the complicated system of straps which emanate from the leather tongue that covers the top of the foot are painted with dilute (orange-brown) glaze to which traces of pink engobe adhere. The narrow and shapely foot, with delicately modelled toes (traces of the modelling tool on toenails, creases in toe straps, etc.), is almost certainly a woman's.

It is preserved intact and partially covered with limy incrustation.

Terracotta; said to be from Sicily; Western Greek; fourth to third century B.C.
Length: 12.5 cm.; height: 7.9 cm.

BIBLIOGRAPHY: Cf. R. A. Higgins, Cat. of the Terracottas in the British Museum II (London, 1959), no. 1680 (from Akragas). Higgins points out that his no. 1680 is derivative, being modelled on a common Eastern Greek type. Right and left feet occur. Cf. also Higgins no. 1655, where a list of Archaic sandal vases is given.
(H. H.)

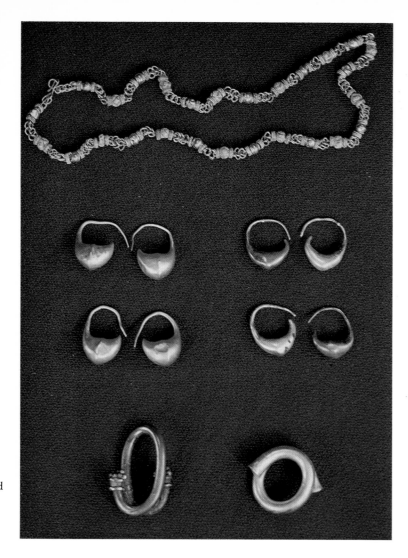

e

a

b

c, d

69   Finds of Gold and Silver Jewellery

a) Two pairs of golden boat-shaped earrings.
Stamped in two halves, with a vertical median seam.
Height: 2.5 cm.

b) Two pairs of silver earrings, similar to the preceding.
Solid-cast.
Height: 2 cm.
The type flourished in Greece and the Near East for several centuries. Cf. Higgins, Greek and Roman Jewellery (London 1961), 122 (1).

c) A pair of silver spiralform earrings. Cast and hammered wire of heavy gauge (Dm. 4 mm.) bent into a loop of one and a half turns. The ends are decorated with pyramidal formations of granules set on a thin base sheet bordered by an ornamental collar.
Similar pyramids decorated the "elbows" of each earring, but only one of these is preserved. The type is rare (cf. Higgins,

Jewellery, 123 (2). As indicated by an *in situ* find at Ialysos, Rhodes, such earrings were not worn directly on the ear but suspended via an s-shaped wire. Height: 3.5 cm.

d) Single earring. Solid-cast. Splayed spiral of one and a half turns, the ends slightly spreading and decorated with an incised zigzag pattern over a base line. For the type, which is documented by other finds, cf. Higgins, Jewellery, fig. 22 D. Said to be from Ephesos. Eastern Greek. 7th-6th century B.C.

e) The necklace consists of fourteen plain and thirteen granulated beads of gold flanked by granulated ring spacers and interspaced by groups of two and three loop-in-loops. The terminals are modern.

Gold; said to be from Sicily; Greek; late 3rd century B.C.
Length: 42.6 cm.

BIBLIOGRAPHY: H. Hoffmann – P. F. Davidson, Greek Gold (1965), no. 52. Cf. Marshall, Cat. Jewellery...British Museum, no. 1979.   (H. H.)

70 Bracelet

Spirally ribbed bracelet terminating in ram's-head finials with annular collars. The ram's fleece is indicated by puncheon marks. A row of granulation was originally laid in the spiral groove between the two twisted wires that form the hoop, but of this only seven beads have been preserved (visible in lower right-hand area in photograph). A close stylistic parallel to this beautiful bracelet is afforded by the crystal example with gold ram's heads in the Ganymede Treasure (R. Zahn, Galerie Bachstitz II, pls. 22–23; G. M. A. Richter, Handbook of the Greek Collection [1953], pl. 129g). The Schimmel bracelet also dates from the general period of Alexander the Great and like the Ganymede Treasure probably comes from Macedonia.

Silver; Greek; late 4th century B.C.
Diameter: 5.5 cm.

BIBLIOGRAPHY: H. Hoffmann – P. F. Davidson, Greek Gold (1965), no. 58.   (H. H.)

71 Bracelet

A massive gold bracelet (or armlet?) cast solid in the form of a snake with open mouth. The scales are indicated at each end of the body, the greater part of which has been left plain. A triangle within scrolls, plus a group of punched dots, are incised on the plain areas of the body just below the scales. The details were chased after casting. A curious feature is the presence of the conspicuous flat protective plates on the snake's head. It is clear enough that the animal belongs to the family *colubridae*, but the genus remains uncertain. Formerly in the J. J. Ackworth Collection.

Gold; Early Ptolemaic Period (ca. 300–250 B.C.); Diameter: 8.6 cm.

BIBLIOGRAPHY: Metropolitan Museum Exhib. Cat., no. 85.   (J. D. C.)

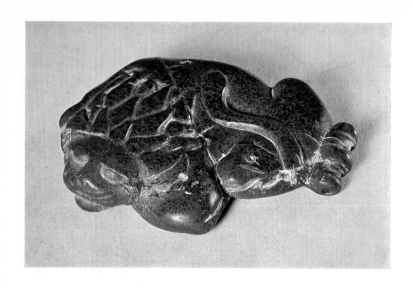

72 Lion Pendant

A couchant lion with its head turned to one side and resting on its paws is shown. The hind legs are neatly tucked under the belly, and the tail is laid onto the back. The mane is rendered in four staggered tiers of lozenge- and drop-shaped curls. The rendering of the eyes, brows and nose is greatly simplified. The object is a pendant and hung nose down (as indicated by the tripartite suspension flange projecting from the rump); it may have been worn from a necklace in the manner of an amulet. There are no restorations, but the piece was broken and repaired.

A small group of amber lion pendants in Copenhagen, Hamburg and London can be ascribed to the same carver: cf. H. Hoffmann, AA (1969) 364 f., fig. 49 a, b and D. E. Strong, Catalogue of the Carved Amber ... British Museum (1966) no. 64. The Schimmel pendant is the largest and finest of them all. Strong (loc. cit.) has associated the London pendant and a group of related carvings (including the amber figures from Belmonte Piceno) with the Acheloos pendant in the British Museum (his cat. no. 68) and assigned these works to a South Italian Greek atelier. B. Shefton, Archaeological Reports 1969/70 (1970) 58, suggests they may be Campanian.

Opaque dark red amber; Central or South Italy, late 6th – early 5th century B.C.
Length: 8 cm.; diameter (max.): 6.6 cm.; thickness (max.): 1.5 cm.

BIBLIOGRAPHY: Cf. also Zadoks - Jitta, BAntBeschav (1962), 61 ff.; L. Brown, The Etruscan Lion (Oxford, 1960), 100.
(H. H.)

73 Ladle

A shallow ladle for thick liquids such as honey. The handle is split at the top and rolled into two scrolls suggestive of an Ionic capital. Originally these must have been surmounted by a ring for hanging when not in use.

The faceted stem was produced by spirally twisting and hammering. The base of the stem spreads into a shallow bowl decorated with the finely chased and gilt representation of a sphinx with raised wings seated before a spray with pointed leaves and enclosed by a wreath of laurel. The front of the bowl has been deliberately nicked and the sides bent slightly upwards, possibly a makeshift improvement by a onetime owner. Although the stylistic conventions of the drawing are difficult to date precisely, the relatively "free" rendering of the sphinx's wings preclude a date before the middle of the fifth century B.C.

Engraved silver vessels and utensils are comparatively short-lived in Greece; they appear about 450 B.C. and disappear again in the fourth century, when relief decoration comes in vogue. Silver ladles (*kyathoi*) become common in the Hellenistic period but are then of a different type; the present example is unique and appears to be modelled on an Achemenian prototype.

Silver; apparently fire-gilt; Greek; later 5th to early 4th century B.C.
Height (vertical): 19.2 cm.

BIBLIOGRAPHY: Cf. D. E. Strong, Greek and Roman Silver Plate (London, 1966), 91 f.   (H. H.)

74 Stalk of Wheat

A stalk of wheat (*triticum compactum*) dividing into three stems with ears is represented. The blades are striated on both sides with delicate, almost imperceptible lines, producing a very realistically textured surface. Each ear consists of twenty-eight kernels delicately wired in nine tiers of four kernels each. The individual kernels consist of unbacked half-shells to which are attached the long rolled wires that form the "silk". Two leaves are missing, otherwise the stalk is intact.

This extraordinary object was found around the year 1900 near Syracuse in Sicily and at one time belonged to the Munich collector James Loeb. When Loeb emigrated to Cambridge, Mass. in 1938 the golden ears were among the few antiquities he took with him, the rest of his collection having been ceded by him to the Munich Antikensammlungen. On his death they passed into the posession of his sister-in-law, Mrs. J. W. Hambuechen.

Paul Wolters, who first published the Loeb ears in a Festschrift dedicated to the celebrated collector deduced that they must have been either a votive deposit or a funerary dedication. He favored the latter explanation on account of the perfect preservation.

Five golden ears of wheat wired together were found in the hands of a female corpse identified as that of a priestess of Demeter, in a Hellenistic tumulus on the Taman peninsula in South Russia (now in the Hermitage). The grain goddess Demeter herself is depicted holding a triple spray on an Attic amphora in Harvard (The Frederick M. Watkins Collection [Cambridge, 1973] no. 29). Whether it is specifically the badge of office of a priestess or, more universally, a funerary symbol expressing a hope for immortality can no longer be established without knowledge of the precise context in which the object was found. Wolters dated the object in the fourth to third century B.C. on the basis of numismatic evidence and sculptural representations. His dating has come to be generally accepted.

These ears have been imitated in several skillful forgeries that have come onto the market in recent years: cf. A. Greifenhagen, Gnomon 40 (1968), 695 ff. and H. Hoffmann AJA 73 (1969) 447 ff.

Gold; Greek; fourth to third century B.C. Said to have been found near Syracuse. Height: 26 cm.

BIBLIOGRAPHY: P. Wolters, in Festschrift James Loeb (Munich, 1930), 111 ff., figs. 1–15, pl. 14; Ancient Art in American Private Collections (1954) no. 310; H. Hoffmann – P. F. Davidson, Greek Gold (1965), no. 137 (with technological commentary); E. Simon, Die Götter der Griechen (1969), 115 ff., fig. 109; Hoffmann, Collecting, color plate 19.   (H. H.)

75 Quartet of "Horse and Rider" Fibulae

These four fibulae are the largest, most elaborate and best-preserved examples of a fanciful type known from scattered examples from Tarquinia and elsewhere in central and northern Etruria. Their contexts, where known, suggest that they were popular early in the seventh century B.C. The basic form, in which the body of an animal (dog or lion?, horse) forms the arc of the fibula, can occur with or without "riders", either a conventional one, astride the middle of the animal's body, or a small ape or ape-like being perched on the animal's rump.

All four fibulae exhibit extensive and meticulous chasing done after their casting; this process is responsible for the forms of the animals' heads, as well as the subsidiary grooves framing their jaws, and the features of the "riders". Except for one fibula, the end of whose catchplate is damaged and whose pin has been mended about one third the distance from spring to tip, the fibulae are intact.

The legs of the animal that forms the bow of the fibula are elongated to form the pin and catchplate. The front leg is bent at right angles to form a long, narrow catchplate; the hind leg narrows to form the pin, whose spring has two turns, coiled counterclockwise. The animal's head has small ears pointing backward, an open mouth, the jaws of which are accentuated by a delicate groove, and a small bead or ruff just under the head. An S-shaped tail, ending in a tuft-like knob, projects from the posterior of the animal. The upper part of the "rider", more monkey-like than humanoid in appearance, rises from the top of the animal's rump; cast separately, its lower part was inserted into a specially prepared hole in the top of the animal's posterior. The rider's rounded head has crudely-worked features: large nose and lips, and facets for eyes. He holds both arms upwards; the left ends in a knob, while the right sprouts an axe-like square blade, turned forward.

Similar fibulae of varying forms include one with a riding ape holding its hands up to its face, from the "Bocchoris Tomb", Monterozzi, Tarquinia, clearly of the first quarter of first third of the seventh century B.C.

Bronze; late Villanovan – early Etruscan, ca. first third of the seventh century B.C.
Length of pin: 11 cm.; height of animal: 5 cm.; height of rider: 2.2 cm.

BIBLIOGRAPHY: For "horse and rider" fibulae; cf. H. Müller-Karpe, Schriftenreihe zur bayerischen Landesgeschichte 62, 101 ff. (reference courtesy of H. O'N. Hencken); D. Rebuffat-Emmanuel, "Singes de Maurétanie Tingitane et d'Italie", StEtr 35 (1967) – 637–638, notes 40–49 (list of such fibulae), and pl. cxxxv,g (Tomba Benacci, no. 520; Bologna). For examples from Tarquinia, cf. H. O'N. Hencken, Tarquinia, Villanovans and Early Etruscans (Cambridge, Mass., Peabody Museum, 1968) 408–409, fig. 404; fibula from "Bocchoris Tomb": ibid., 367, fig. 361; discussion of related "lion fibulae" ("terminus post quem in closing years of eighth century"), 346–347, fig. 347, g. Cf. also Museum of Fine Arts, Boston, no. 13.139, part of a fibula similar to the Schimmel fibulae; M. Comstock – C. C. Vermeule, Greek Etruscan and Roman Bronzes in the Museum of Fine Arts, Boston (Greenwich, Conn., New York Graphic Society, 1971), no. 194, pp. 168–169. (D. G. M.)

76 Buckle with Horse Heads

Bluish-green patina. The hooks of this large ornamental buckle have the form of horse-heads. The horses' ears are formed by stylized birds. Details crudely incised.

Bronze; said to be from Populonia; Villanovan; 9th–8th centuries B.C.
Width: 8.2 cm.

BIBLIOGRAPHY: Queens College Exhib. Cat., no. 135. Cf. British Museum 1958 8–22, 12 and 13.   (H. H.)

77 Bull Pendant

Foreparts of two long-horned bovids back to back, with a hole for suspension (clogged by remains of the iron suspension ring) through the common hump they share. Ornamental pendants such as this unusually large specimen were popular in Villanovan Italy and probably had a magical function. Bronzes of similar type occur in Sardinia, the Balkans and Iran during the Late Bronze and Early Iron ages.

Bronze; said to be from Picenum; Villanovan; 9th–8th centuries B.C.
Height: 6.5 cm.; length: 10.5 cm.

BIBLIOGRAPHY: Cf. Herbert Cahn, Auktion XXII der Münzen und Medaillen A.G. Basel, 13 May 1961, no. 64 (with other parallels, to which can be added Libertini, Museo Biscari, pl. 55, no. 347).   (H. H.)

78   One-handled Cup

The cast handle is rivetted onto the hammered bowl. The bowl of the cup is shallow, with steep, convex sides; it sits upon a hollow, conical foot that is probably attached with solder. The exterior of the cup is decorated with finely incised horizontal lines, which are connected by short vertical lines. The rectangular panels thus formed are filled by very delicate diagonal parallel striations. The handle, probably cast in a two-piece mold, has two uprights rivetted onto the bowl; the tip of the handle is an oval openwork plaque whose central part is formed by a miniature stylized horse in the Villanovan "Geometric" style, best known from the elaborate cast cheek-pieces from contemporary flexible bits.

The one-handled cup was a shape peculiar to the central Italic Iron Age and the succeeding archaic Etruscan culture. In addition to numerous ceramic variants, two basic Villanovan forms of one-handled cups in bronze are known: an earlier, simple flat-bottomed shape, followed by later, more elaborate cups, often on a hollow conical foot, among which the Schimmel cup belongs. A fairly close parallel to the Schimmel cup, from Vetulonia, is in the Museo Archeologico, Florence. A closely parallel cast openwork handle decorates a flat-bottomed bronze cup with embossed decoration in the University of Missouri Museum.

On the basis of Hencken's typology for Villanovan bronze cups from Tarquinia, the Schimmel cup is to be dated in Villanovan II, ca. 750–700 B.C., the exact workshop from which it comes, however, remains to be determined.

Bronze; Italic; Villanovan II, ca. 750–700 B.C.
Total height: 13.7 cm.; diameter of bowl: 13.7 cm.; diameter of foot: 7 cm.; maximum width of handle: 8.2 cm.

BIBLIOGRAPHY: Cf. H. O'N. Hencken, Tarquinia, Villanovans and Early Etruscans (Cambridge, Mass., Peabody Museum, 1968), 544–545. For the incised decoration of the Schimmel cup, cf. Hencken, op. cit., 545–547. For the openwork handle type, cf. D. Randall–MacIver, Villanovans and Early Etruscans (Oxford, 1924), 141, pl. 26, 8, Mostra dell' Etruria Padana e della Citta di Spina (Bologna, 1960), I, no. 845; 258–259, pl. XII; Cup at University of Missouri: Museum of Art and Archaeology, inv. no. 65.15; Master Bronzes, no. 156, p. 157. For the Villanovan cheek-pieces in the form of horses, cf. F. W. von Hase, Die Trensen der Früheisenzeit in Italien (Munich, 1968), passim. G. von Merhart, "Zu einem etruskischen Henkeltypus", Hallstatt und Italien (Mainz, Verlag des Römisch-Germanischen Zentralmuseums, 1969), 268–279.   (D. G. M.)

80 Woman with Tutulus

Solid-cast; lustrous grey-green patina. Missing right hand. Elongated female figure wearing a sleeved garment reaching above the ankles, tutulus with scalloped brim and pointed boots. Her arms are raised and bent at the elbow. Flat hand, with fingers bent backwards. The features – small nose, almond eyes and narrow mouth – are summarily rendered. The hair is indicated in the front only, as a narrow cross-hatched band.

Bronze; Etruscan; 5th century B.C.
Height: 17.1 cm.

BIBLIOGRAPHY: Worcester Cat. no. 63, pl. 9.   (H. H.)

79 Naked Warrior

Solid-cast. He steps forward in combat position. His shield and spear are missing. Mouth, eyes, brows and forehead hair incised. "A good, rather provincial, example of the Ionian style in Etruria, which corresponds quite closely with Miss Richter's 'Anavysos-Ptoon 12' group of Greek kouroi. Arezzo 11 549 is slightly earlier, Fiesole 485 slightly later." (E. Richardson). The casting tenons have been left in place under the feet to secure the figure to its base (cf. no. 60).
Formerly in the collection of V. Simkhovitch.

Bronze; Etruscan; 2nd half of the 6th century B.C.
Height: 16.5 cm.

BIBLIOGRAPHY: Master Bronzes no. 159; Worcester. Cat. no. 9; H. Jucker, AA, 1967, 211, fig. 29 a–c; ibid., Art and Technology, fig. 29 a–c.   (H. H.)

81 Woman with Tutulus

Solid-cast; pitted. She stands with left foot slightly advanced and lifts her long closely fitting garment with both hands. She wears pointed boots and a pointed hat or tutulus. The lead plug, which secured the figure to its base, is preserved, as, probably, are the casting-tenons (cf. no. 79). "Catania 1569 has much the same proportions; Florence 257 is slightly later, but the opulent proportions are not unlike." (E. Richardson).

Bronze; said to be from Campiglia Marittima near Populonia; Etruscan, perhaps workshops of Vulci; 2nd half of the 6th century B.C.
Height (max.): 13.7 cm.

BIBLIOGRAPHY: Queens College Exhib. Cat., no. 139. H. Jucker, Art and Technology, figs. 7 a—c; ibid., AA, 1967, 622, figs. 3—4.

(H.H.)

82   Woman Wearing a Diadem

Elongated figure with toes pointing in and arms held out sideways from the body. She wears a crescent-shaped diadem decorated with incised zigzags and a short-sleeved garment reaching to the ankles and decorated in front and back with vertical rows of punched dots. "Villa Giulia 24471 is similar; cf. also Catania 1508 and Arezzo 11806, a more debased variant." (E. Richardson).

Bronze; Umbro-Etruscan; middle of the 5th century B.C.
Height: 19 cm.

BIBLIOGRAPHY: Queens College Exhib. Cat., no. 141; The Etruscan, Artists of Early Italy, Walters Art Gallery Exhib. Cat., 1958, no. 122.

(H.H.)

83–85   Reclining Lions   85 bis   Flower

Lions were a favorite subject in Greek and Etruscan art. Elegantly stylized examples such as these owe a great deal to Eastern prototypes. Their flat, heart-shaped ears follow late Hittite models, while the elaborate surface patterning and the subdivision of the body by grooves more generally reflect Assyrian types.

The fore and hind paws of the Schimmel lions are not separately articulated; each pair is treated as a single simplified volume. The mane is depicted in parallel rows of tiny crescents, executed with a punch. The upper and lower rows are turned at a 90° angle to the others, and delicate curls composed of crescents lie along each side of the raised back-bone of the single lions. The double lion's backbone is a pronounced double groove, while two double grooves encircle its mid-section. The deep-set eyes are bulbous; eyebrows are indicated. A stylized ridge over the brow, continuing around the jowls, may be a vestigial ruff.

A bulbous "beard" adorns the chin. Three unbroken, straight grooves across the muzzle indicate the mouth, with diagonal grooves above as whiskers, and a row of punched semi-circles below. Two small concentric crescents occur on the forehead, between the eyes.

The lions were once attached to something made of iron. A heavy iron rivet pierces each set of forepaws, and substantial traces of an iron plate remain beneath the two single lions.

Even more puzzling is the fact that the traces of an iron pin can be seen in the center of each fore and hind flank, indicating that the lions may have been attached to each other by rods, or that something – a handle, perhaps – was attached to them. Other pins in the caudal region of the two single lions may have served for attaching separately cast tails. It is not immediately clear what function these lions might have served. They may perhaps have reclined upon the corners and sides of a *focolare,* or wheeled hearth, or have adorned an elaborate ceremonial chariot. Single lions on *focolari* are well known, but the double-headed lion is more unusual. Its cleat-like shape would have been an ideal anchor around which to secure a chariot's reins.

The lions are solid cast and heavily corroded with blue-green patina that shows azurite patches and iron oxide deposits. They were found with a five-petalled bronze flower with iron stamen on a rectangular plinth. While the exact method of attachment remains unknown, one may surmise that this blossom formed part of the decoration of the chariot to which the lions are said to have belonged.

Bronze, Etruscan, ca. 550–500 B.C.

Reclining lion A: Length: 10.8 cm.; height: 6.4 cm.; width: 4.6 cm.	Flower: Height: 12.6 cm.
Reclining lion B: Length: 10.4 cm.; height: 6.3 cm.; width: 4.5 cm.	
Double-headed lion: Length: 12.3 cm.; height: 5.7 cm.; width: 3.8 cm.	

BIBLIOGRAPHY: For similar lions, cf. W. L. Brown, The Etruscan Lion (Oxford, 1960), pp. 90–95, esp. 94, n. 1, on focolari; pls. 37 a–b (lions on focolari); similar Greek lions: H. Gabelmann, Studien zum früh-griechischen Löwenbild (Berlin, 1965), pls. 9, 20 ff. For an East Greek bronze lion especially close to the Etruscan types, cf. Museum of Fine Arts Boston, inv. no. 66.9; Master Bronzes, no. 60, p. 69; M. Comstock – C. C. Vermeule, Greek, Etruscan and Roman Bronzes in the Museum of Fine Arts, Boston (Boston, MFA, 1971), no. 433, pp. 307–308.

(S. D. and D. G. M.)

86 Mounted Archer

Dull, dark green surface, the patina largely removed. Rider and leaping horse cast separately, the latter with a thin rectangular platform which is partially preserved. The rider, an archer in Scythian dress, wears a jerkin and a Phrygian cap, both decorated with puncheon mark. Presumably trousers are also intended. The mane and tail, as well as the details of harness, are engraved.

Bronze; from Suessula; Campanian; early 5th century B.C.
Height: 12.6 cm.

BIBLIOGRAPHY: F. v. Duhn, Römische Mitteilungen 2 (1887) 244, fig. 18 b; Metropolitan Museum Exhib. Cat., no. 149. Worcester Cat. no. 36 (with complete bibliography).   (H. H.)

87   Handle of a Stamnos

Lustrous greenish-blue patina. Handle and attachments cast in one. The latter have the form of symmetrically disposed addorsed hippocamps in high relief, their heads, facing frontally, worked in the round. Manes, brows, flippers, fins and tail fins carefully engraved. Each hippocamp wears two collars, an upper one of small punched circles between two engraved lines and a lower one of punched disc ornaments each suspended by two crescents from a single engraved line. The handle was attached to the stamnos by two large rivets, one above each hippocamp's flipper, and of these the right one is still in place.

Bronze; Etruscan; workshop of Vulci; early 5th century B.C.
Height: 10 cm.; length: 16.2 cm.

BIBLIOGRAPHY: Worcester Cat., no. 52; Master Bronzes, no. 197.   (H. H.)

88 Reclining Satyr

This solid cast satyr half reclines in a jaunty, alert pose. Hoofed feet and equine ears betray his semi-human nature, although there is no trace of a tail. He holds a drinking horn in his right hand and extends his left, with closed fist, the forearm propped on his raised knee.

The satyr's right elbow rests on a curving, hollowed form terminating in front in three rounded projections and in back in two. The analogy of countless other bronze banqueters – human and satyr – suggests that it may represent a cushion or rock, although the shape more nearly resembles a small animal pelt. A hole through this element served for rivetting the figure to a rounded surface of some vessel or utensil. Reclining figures are used frequently by the Etruscans to adorn hanging lamps, braziers, handles, vessel feet, the rims of kraters, and both the upper rim and base rings of the rod-tripods. The Dionysiac satyrs formed a particularly appropriate decoration for vessels for serving wine at banquets, and for the tripods on which they rested.

Bronze; Etruscan, perhaps from Vulci, ca. 500 B.C.
Height: 4 cm.; length: 4.7 cm.

BIBLIOGRAPHY: Cf. Bibliothèque Nationale (E. Babelon – J. A. Blanchet, Catalogue des bronzes antiques de la Bibliothèque Nationale (Paris, 1895), 182–3, no. 414; Käppeli Collection (now Basel, Antikenmuseum) Kunstwerke der Antike (Basel, 1963), B 12; C. H. Smith, Bronzes, antique Greek, Roman, etc. ... Collection of J. Pierpont Morgan (Paris, 1913), 11, no. 25; and City Art Museum of St. Louis (Master Bronzes, 98, no. 95). For reclining figures, U. Jantzen, Griechische Greifenkessel (Berlin, 1955), 101, no. 146, supplemented by E. Kunze, VIII. Bericht über die Ausgrabungen in Olympia (Berlin, 1967), 241, no. 57. For satyrs on a lamp, K. A. Neugebauer, AA (1924), 313–314, fig. 5; on a brazier, K. A. Neugebauer, RM 51 (1936), 181 ff., pls. 24–26; on a vessel foot, P. J. Riis, AASyr. 8–9 (1958–59), 129, fig. 14; reclining figures on a handle, G. Q. Giglioli, L'arte etrusca (Milan, 1935), pl. 209:2; on tripod stands, P. J. Riis, ActaArch 10 (1939), 1–30, fig. 6 and 11; K. A. Neugebauer, Jdl 58 (1943), 206 ff., figs. 12, 17, 18; satyrs lying on leopard skins: A. G. Bather, JHS 13 (1892–93), 240 and fig. 12. (S. D.)

89 Pair of Handles of a Column Krater

Light olive-green patina. Each handle platform is supported by two caryatid silenoi who make the silen's characteristic gesture of aposkopein, or "peering into the distance" (see I. Jucker, Der Gestus des Aposkopein, 1956). Their hair, moustaches and beards are finely striated. Their hooved feet rest on inverted volute palmettes which served as the bottom handle attachments, and their bushy tails are arranged along their outer flanks. Bothmer thinks that an ornament or statuette might have been fastened to the platforms, one of which (as he observes) has an incised chi (or simply a cross?) on top.

Bronze; Etrusco-Campanian; early 5th century B.C.
Heights: 10.2 and 10.4 cm. respectively.

BIBLIOGRAPHY: Metropolitan Museum Exhib. Cat., no. 152. Worcester Cat. no. 37; Master Bronzes no. 200 a–b.   (H. H.)

90 Banqueter Relief

Thin ivory panel, probably an inlay. Two banqueters within a frame of concave tongues, some of the tongues preserving traces of a gold foil overlay. They wear chitons lowered to the waist, and pointed caps. The left banqueter appears to hold a small bowl; both gesture animatedly. At the left, a plant with oval fruit, perhaps a grapevine.

Ivory; Etruscan; ca. 500 B.C.
Length: 6.8 cm.; height: 3.3 cm.

BIBLIOGRAPHY: Worcester Cat., no. 40. Cf. Revue des Arts 3 (1955), 134, fig. 4 (Louvre, from Tarquinia).   (H.H.)

91 Lion Finial

The flat object is topped by a slender human finger which rests against the rump of a three-dimensional crouching lion facing out. The lion's fur is rendered by hatching; the mane is carved in bold relief. The two sides of the carving are virtually alike; both are worked with the same attention to detail. The original context may have been a piece of furniture or possibly a musical instrument. The material has aged a mellow yellow-orange and slabbed horizontally into a great many layers which have been glued together.

Ivory; Roman; Imperial period.
Height: 5 cm.; length: 8.9 cm.; thickness: 9 mm.   (H. H.)

92 A Fish Vial

A small vessel of fish form in blue-green glass, probably mould-blown. The fins and tail were drawn into form with pincers. The glass is now cloudy and opaque but was probably once clear.
This vessel and its companion pieces are of Roman date but they recall their ancestors of the Egyptian New Kingdom with which they have no connection either in technique or in the type of fish represented. But each served as a container though precisely how and for what liquid are unclear. They must have been supplied with a stand which held them upright and were doubtless stoppered with a wad of linen.

Glass; Roman work probably of Syrian origin, ca. 2nd century A.D.
Length: 10 cm.   (J. C.)

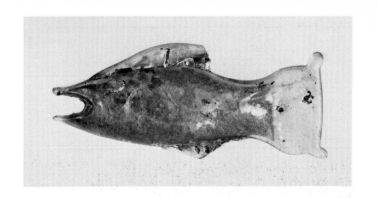

93 Fish Bottle

Tip of the nose restored. Mould-blown glass of greenish amber color with whitish overlay and silver-blue irridescence. Such fish bottles were made throughout the Roman empire and were especially popular in Syria.

Said to be from the Hauran; Syro-Roman; 3rd century A.D.
Length: 27.6 cm.

BIBLIOGRAPHY: Journal of Glass Studies 2 (1960), 138, fig. 7.
                                                         (H. H.)

94   Cameo Portrait of Caracalla

The bust is terminated at the bottom by a stylized animal skin (?), perhaps an allusion to Herakles. The schematic treatment of the hair as a lozenge pattern is unusual. The nose is chipped.

Onyx; Roman or Post-Antique.
Height: 2.9 cm.; diameter: 2.1 cm.; thickness: 9 mm.

BIBLIOGRAPHY: Cf. E. Babelon, Cat. des camées antiques et modernes . . . Bibliothèque Nationale (Paris, 1897), no. 302; for an uncertain Caracalla cf. F. Eichler – E. Kris, Die Kameen im Kunsthistorischen Museum (Vienna, 1927), no. 76.   (H. H.)

95   Portrait of Caracalla

Only the front of the head is preserved; the countenance is somewhat flattened through crushing. The piece, a fragment of a portrait statue, has been associated with a group of monumental bronze sculptures said to have been found together in the ruins of a Severan villa in western Asia Minor. These are now dispersed throughout the United Staates. See C. Vermeule, Roman Imperial Art from Greece and Asia Minor (Cambridge, 1968).
Caracalla (emperor A. D. 211—217) is at once recognizable by a series of features familiar from his numerous "canonical" likenesses in stone and on coins: curly hair, furrowed forehead, knit brows, moustache, narrow clipped beard, firm chin and thick neck. This portrait differs somewhat from the others in that the brutal and suspicious traits are somewhat subdued and the moustache is not drawn over the corners of the mouth. As pointed out by H. Menzel, "The relative calm of . . . physiognomy is a characteristic of Roman imperial sculpture from the Greek East" (as opposed to the harsher and more realistic tendencies displayed by portraits of the same subject from the West). Several casting flaws were repaired in antiquity with rectangular patches.

Bronze; hollow cast; said to be from Asia Minor; Roman; early third century A.D.
Height: 21.6 cm.

BIBLIOGRAPHY: Master Bronzes, no. 234 (H. Menzel).   (H. H.)

96   Head of a Roman Youth

This strikingly handsome, refined portrait head of a Roman youth reflects the romanticism of the Hadrianic-Antonine age. Gazing slightly to his right, with large, deep-set eyes, soft full pouting lips, and a crown of thick tousled curls, the youth invokes the elevated heroic mood of a semidivine being. The soft, rounded form of the face, the firm forehead and high cheekbones intensify the expression of thoughtfulness and sensitivity.

The head is characterized by a number of rich details. The rendering of the individual hairs of the eyebrows, the large protruding ears, and the dissolved masses of hair serve to elevate this youthful figure from a generalized Greek prototype to a distinctive personality. A running drill, producing vivid contrasts of highlights and shadows, was lavishly used to create the luxuriant, abundant locks. A kind of colouristic pictorialism is achieved through the transformation of a solid block of stone into the twisted, hollowed masses of hair.

The plastic rendering of the eye, marking the iris by a lightly incised circle, and the deepening of the pupil by single or double drill holes, often set into a crescent-shaped depression, give the portrait a particularly striking sense of individuality and emotional expression.

The portrait clearly belongs to the early Antonine Age. Portraits of young Marcus Aurelius are so similar that one has to consider whether this head might not be a variant of an Imperial portrait type. It is now understood that most Imperial portraits preserved are copies of a limited number of lost "official" originals; and such copies can display an amazing range of differences. One might consider whether the Schimmel portrait could be a brilliant, idiosyncratic version of the "Capitolino, Galleria 28" type, which showed Marcus as a boy, and of which the original is dated by M. Wegner to A.D. 140 (Die Herrscherbildnisse in antoninischer Zeit. [Berlin, 1939] 36–38, pl. 15); but the locks over the forehead (in the Schimmel portrait) do not have the right direction; and this is the kind of detail that was not readily changed in the portrait of a prince.

The young sitter, then, a contemporary of young Marcus, must remain unnamed. Not only a striking detail – the very opulent cap of locks – but also the general romantic concept of the adolescent owes a debt to the tradition of the Antinous portraits. Mood

and style (which is "city-Roman" even if the marble is not) are close to heads claimed recently as possibly representing children of Antoninus Pius. The ambient is that of court sculptors influenced by Hadrianic tradition.

A similar romantic vision underlies the portraits of Polydeukes (or Polydeukion), the favorite pupil and relative of the millionaire-sophist Herodes Atticus (A. D. 107–177), the benefactor of Athens. The precise sharpness of cutting in the Schimmel portrait, however, is quite different from the softer style of even the best Athenian portraits of the Antonine age.

The marble has a grainy, uniform, unpolished texture, and a yellowish surface. Some abrasion and chipping on the chin, cheeks, bridge of nose, eye area, lips. Spectrographic examination revealed few modern damages: a very fresh break on top of head, and a small ancient break on back of head.

Marble; Roman, ca. 140–170 A.D.
Height (chin to top of head): 27.94 cm.; width (ear to ear): 21.6 cm.

BIBLIOGRAPHY: For the Antinous portraits, cf. Ch. W. Clairmont, Die Bildnisse des
Antinous (Rome, 1966), 24–26, pls. 2, 5, 9, 18. For possible portraits of children of
Antoninus Pius, cf. H. von Heintze in Th. Kraus, Das römische Weltreich (Berlin,
1967), 258–259, pls. 310–311. For Antonine portraits, cf. E. B. Harrison, Portrait
Sculpture, The Athenian Agora I (Princeton, N. J., 1953), 28–41, no. 28, pl. 19, with
references; and 37–38, no. 26, pl. 18: Polydeukion; his other portraits, K. A. Neuge-
bauer, F. Arndt-Bruckmann, Griechische und römische Porträts, ed. P. Arndt and
G. Lippold, pls. 1198–1199, and text; C. C. Vermeule, "A Greek Theme and Its Surviv-
als: The Ruler's Shield (Tondo Image) in Tomb and Temple", Proceedings of the
American Philosophical Society 109:6 (December, 1965), 394–395 fig. 52.
(J. W. B. and G. M. A. H.)

97   Head of a Young Man

This compact, nearly life-size head of a young-man, with jaw firmly set and eyes wandering slightly upward to his right, is somewhat remote and contemplative in expression. The pale, cool polished surface of the marble is touched slightly by a greyish-blue tinge. The strong, crooked nose ultimately emphasizes the irregular, assymetric character of the features. The powerful, plastic quality of his high cheekbones, forceful brow, pursed lips and heavy eyelids, with lids, pupils and tear ducts carefully represented, reveals a rather pensive, day-dreaming character. His small ears are tucked beneath a thick, clipped cap of well-defined locks. A square hole is to be found on the "sliced-off" posterior plane, which extends not quite to the lower hairline and is carefully smoothed around the edges and roughened in the center. Traces of sintering encroaching upon the surface suggest that the cut is ancient.

Less heroic and majestic than Imperial portraits, this head conveys a mood of dignity, individuality, and nobility marked by distinctly human accents, such as a softening at the mouth's corners and the wandering glance; the supple, soft modelling of the flesh gives the figure a sense of cool detachment. The facial planes are flat, and there is an exquisite subtlety of the overall effect of skin over bone.

The hair rigidly formal, the upper lip and chin cleanshaven, the wide-eyed gaze are channels through which the underlying spirit is communicated. The broad, fluid, rhythmic modelling of the central features is tempered by a subdued inquietude of mood. The Schimmel head is arrogant and vain, proud and haughty. His eyes wander upward, his lips pout; a lazy, restless boredom permeates his strong physical features.

In recent times, a number of portraits have presented challenging problems of differentiation between the Trajanic-Hadrianic and the Constantinian Classicisms. P. H. von Blanckenhagen declared a portrait of Trajan to be "late antique" ("Ein spätantikes Bildnis Trajans," JdI, 59–60 [1944–1945] 45), while H. Jucker ("Zwei konstantinische Porträtköpfe in Karthago," Gestalt und Geschichte, Festschrift K. Schefold, Antike Kunst Beiheft 4 [1967] 128) reinstated as Trajan the "Constantine" in Cividale, and E. B. Harrison tried to claim parts of the colossus of Constantine in the Conservatori Museum and the head of "Constantia" in Chicago as respectively Trajanic and Hadrianic

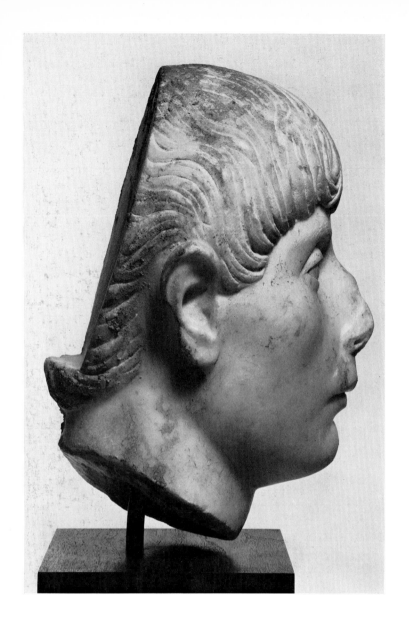
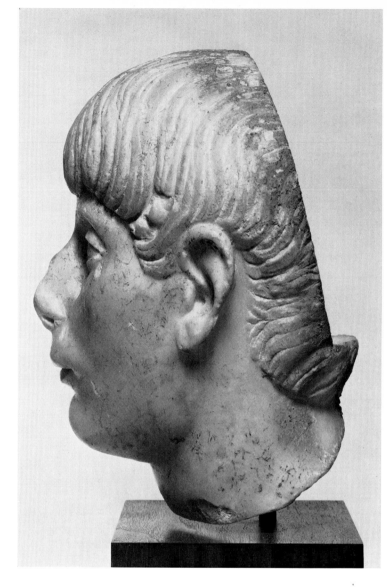

works ("The Constantinian Portrait," Dumbarton Oaks Papers 21 [1967] 85–89, 92–94, figs. 31, 41–44). The Schimmel portrait enters into this controversial area.

At first, the brilliant, glossy surface and the hardness of major forms suggest considering the head a work of Constantinian Classicism, close to "Constantia", following a suggestion by H. Jucker, by letter. A detailed study of Trajanic and Hadrianic portraits, however, leads to the conclusion that the head is by a master of the time of Hadrian. The hairdo, to be sure, is still Trajanic, but the fine, thin rendering of the eyebrows, the soft chiselwork in the crescents of the pupils, and the brightly polished surface fit only an early- or mid-Hadrianic (A.D. 120–130) date. The head belongs to a series of portraits of boys and young men which extends from ca. A.D. 100–130: some of them have similar facial features and expressions.

Even the most similar fourth century heads, such as that of Valentinian II in Toronto, display, especially in profile, a far simpler and more massive, "cubistic" structure and the bored, "spoiled brat", essentially realistic expression of the Schimmel portrait is out of tune with late antique transcendentalism.

Abrasions on nose, lower neck, ears, upper lip, chin, cheeks. Tiny discrete scratches possibly caused by cleaning on face and hair. Root marks from burial evident on cheeks and nose. Spectrographic examination revealed no modern damage.

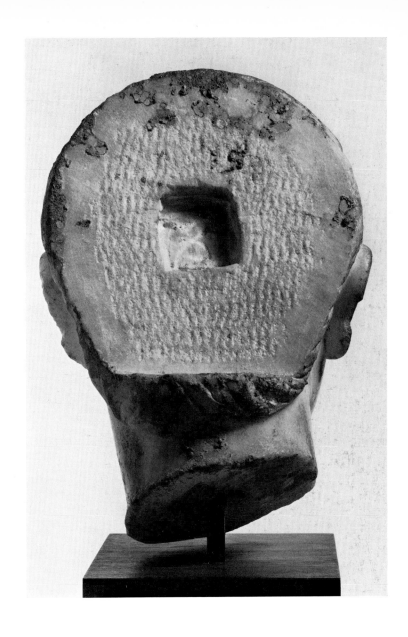

Marble; Roman; 100–130 A.D.
Height (chin to top of head): 22.5 cm.; width (ear to ear):
16.5 cm.

Bibliography: for series of male portraits, ca. 100–130 A.D.:
G. Daltrop, Die stadtrömischen männlichen Privatbildnisse Tra-
janischer und Hadrianischer Zeit (Münster, 1958), 112; 115–
117; 120; 122, with references, figs. 5, 13–16, 20, 57–58; H.
Jucker. Das Bildnis im Blätterkelch (Olten and Freiburg i. Br.,
1961), 1, 71, St 18 A, pl. 26 (Los Angeles); for "cubistic"
structure of fourth century heads, cf. C.C. Vermeule, "Greek
and Roman Portraits in North American Collections", Proceedings of the American Philosophical Society 108:2 (1964),
115, no. 109, fig. 45.   (J. W. B. and G. M. A. H.)

98 Furniture Support: Pappasilenos

This grotesque attachment combines two incongruous elements: the upper part of an obese pappasilenos projects from a massive, four-clawed animal foot. A three-petalled calyx below the pappasilenos' waist achieves an effective transition between the two elements. The pappasilenos' egg-shaped head is bald except for a wide, tongue-like hair mass down the nape of his neck, and a sideburn-like fringe of long curls between his ears and mustache. He has no visible neck. The texture of long locks is shown by incisions, areas of shorter hair by stippling. His drooping, spaniel-like ears repeat the lines of his "sideburns" and his long mustaches. A luxuriant goatee trails from his lower lip to between his breasts. He appears to support his ample paunch with his two hands, held akimbo at the sides; their thumbs point upward, their fourth and fifth fingers are bent back. His torso is featureless except for three small curling tufts of hair that sprout from his navel. Grooves separate the claws on the animal foot from the remainder of their toes.

This unusual support is of great interest from both technological and iconographic points of view. Hollow-cast, with arms separately cast and attached, probably with solder, the piece approaches the scale and complexity of monumental cast bronze sculpture. The animal foot has a long history of use as a termination for the legs of chairs, couches, tables, etc., reaching back at least to eighteenth dynasty Egypt. Our Pappasilenos, probably to be identified as such by his elongated animal ears, bald head, snub nose and pot belly, is also reminiscent of the Egyptian god Bes in proportions, pose and expression. Such a composite conception could well have originated in the

"eclectic", creative climate of Alexandria, which especially favored subject matter with a grotesque or ethnic emphasis, often flavored with a dash of Egyptian influence.

While smaller supports of this form are known, probably products of foundries active in Roman imperial times, this example is the only one of such imposing size and carefully-executed detail known to the writer. While its exact function remains unknown, it most likely served, perhaps with three others, as a caryatid or atlantid-type support for an elaborate table or footstool.

The surface of the bronze varies from light to dark green. There is a hole in the bottom of the foot, and part of the back of the foot is broken away. Ceramic core material has been dug away from the inside of the foot, but still adheres in the interior of the hollow-cast claws and in the middle of the figure. A square perforation, 0.007 m. wide, exists in the top of the head. The main figure is hollow-cast; the arms are made separately, probably hollow-cast, and are attached at the shoulders.

Bronze; late Hellenistic, perhaps from Alexandria; first century Height: 25 cm.; width across elbows: 15.7 cm.　　　[B.C.

BIBLIOGRAPHY: Parallels include P. Perdrizet, Bronzes grecs d'Égypte de la collection Fouquet (Paris, 1911) pl. IX, 21; E. Babelon — J. A. Blanchet, Catalogue des bronzes antiques de la Bibliothèque Nationale (Paris, 1895) no. 389; H. Rolland, Bronzes antiques de Haute Provence (Paris, 1965) no. 398, p. 172 (Musée Calvet d'Avignon, inv. 162 A; found at Bouffaric, Algeria). N. Schimmel mentions two supports in Athens (National Museum, Egyptian Section) similar to this piece, but about half its size and furnished with wings.　　　(D. G. M.)

99 Key

The massive iron shaft makes a right-angle turn downward, then branches to the side. The key terminates in six vertical prongs, three of which have been broken away. The iron shaft, 2.5 cm. wide by 1.5 cm. thick, has been heavily corroded. The bronze handle consists of a reclining bull, grayish-brown in color, facing away from the end of the key. It appears from preliminary examination that the iron shaft is tenoned into a hole in the rump of the bull. The bull is intact except for its left horn, which has been broken off. All four legs are tucked under the body; the genitalia are represented. Details of its anatomy, particularly the folds in the dewlap under the chin, are delicately rendered in the casting.

Animal protomes or figures frequently form the handles for keys of varying sizes during the Roman period, lions and hounds being favorites perhaps because of their reputations as guardians. While keys approaching this size are known furnished with plain wooden knobs as handles (from the "Bar Kochba" cave finds near the Dead Sea, Israel, now in the Israel Museum, Jerusalem, early second century A.D. at latest; parallel courtesy of N. Schimmel), no other keys of this scale, or with this kind of bull handle are known to the writer. An iron key from Bavai has a reclining lion grasping its prey as handle; its legs are tucked under the body in exactly the same way as those of the Schimmel bull. The size of this key suggests use to open a door of large dimensions; the choice of a bull for the handle may possibly reflect association with some cult such as that of Mithras or Serapis, in which the bull figures prominently.

Bronze, Iron; Roman, second – early third century A.D.
Length: 22.5 cm.; height of key: 1.5 cm.; width of pronged terminal: 6.7 cm.; length of bull handle: 10 cm.; width of bull (across hindquarters): 3.1 cm.; height of bull: 4.6 cm.

BIBLIOGRAHPY: For Roman keys, cf. H. Menzel, Die römischen Bronzen aus Deutschland I; Speyer (Mainz, 1960) 27 f.; also Menzel, op. cit., II: Trier (Mainz, 1966) nos. 215–218, pp. 88–89, Taf. 66; other examples: G. Feyder-Faitmans, Receuil des bronzes de Bavai (Paris, 1957) 107–111, pl. XLI–XLII, especially no. 253, pl. XLI, p. 108 (key with reclining lion as handle); E. Espérandieu – H. Rolland, Bronzes antiques de la Seine maritime (Paris, 1959) pl. LI, no. 163, p. 76.   (D. G. M.)

100   Dolphin Handle

Handle attachment of a basin or other large vessel. The heads of the leaping dolphins join the crescent-shaped and slightly convex attachment plate which is decorated in relief with a marine scene consisting of a cuttlefish and two scaly fish emerging from a background of waves. The eyes of the dolphins, as well as of the three fish, are inlaid with silver.
No exact parallels for this interesting object are known.

Bronze; probably Augustan; height 13.5 cm.

BIBLIOGRAPHY: Auktion XXII der Münzen und Medaillen A.G. Basel, 13 May 1961, no. 86 (with more detailed discussion). Master Bronzes no. 288; E. K. Gazda – G. M. A. Hanfmann, Art and Technology, fig. 17.   (H. H.)

101　Furniture Attachment: Bust of Silenos

The silen's mouth is open, giving the impression of deep breathing. His brow is furrowed; his prominent ears curve forward. Groups of ivy berries form a crown on his head. Ribbon ends hang down over his shoulders from a point where they are gathered at the back of his head. He wears the skin of an animal, perhaps a deer, fastened at the right shoulder; the hooves of the skin hang from a circular brooch. Incised lines effectively depict thick tufts of hair on the chest as well as finer hair on the skin garment. A few curved incisions suffice for hair on the silen's head. The bust is hollow cast from behind.

This bust is a finely detailed, unusually small example of a class of decorative bronze attachments commonly associated with elaborate couches (*klinai*) used by reclining diners and revellers, as well as for sleeping. Such busts were most frequently attached to the lower ends of curving bronze plates that adorned the head-pieces (*fulcra*) of such couches. Silenoi form an integral part of the Dionysiac decorative imagery appropriate to the occasions when such couches were most frequently in use. More elaborate bronze attachments were often enriched with inlaid features in silver, copper, and other metals.

Bronze; Roman, first – second century A.D.
Height: 5.8 cm.; width: 4 cm.; height of head (tip of beard to crown): 3 cm.
Width of head: 2.3 cm.

BIBLIOGRAPHY: For couches and their figurative attachments see G. M. A. Richter, *Furniture of the Greeks, Etruscans and Romans* (New York, Phaidon, 1966), 106–109. For silenos bust attachments, cf. E. Diehl, "Bronzener Silenskopf von der Lehne eines römischen Bettes", *Jahrbuch des Römisch-Germanischen Zentralmuseums Mainz*, 7 (1960), 208–213.　　　　　　　　　　　(M. O'L.)

NEAR EAST

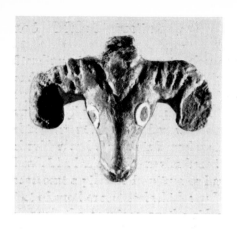

102 Ram's-Head Pendant

The source of lapis lazuli for both Mesopotamia and Iran was eastern Afghanistan, and it was used early and continuously in the Near East. With this small pendant, a ram's head, the artisan has heightened the natural beauty of the blue stone by inlaying the eyes with circles of gold. A small projection on top of the head is pierced. The nostrils and the bottom of the jaw have incised details.

A ram's-head pendant in the Metropolitan Museum, acc. no. 55.65.8, is datable to the second half of the 3rd millennium B.C., because of its close resemblance to a lapis head excavated at Hissar in Iran. It has plain circle-eyes similar to the piece in this collection, but the shape differs slightly from our example. An Iranian provenance is also likely for the latter, the date of which may lie in the 3rd millennium B.C.

Lapis lazuli; Iran (?); 3rd millennium B.C.
Height: 3 cm.

BIBLIOGRAPHY: Metropolitan Museum Exhib. Cat. no. 17. Cf. Erich F. Schmidt, Excavations at Tepe Hissar (1937) 223, fig. 134.　　　　　　(P. O. H.)

103　Amulet-Seal in the Form of a Ram-Head

The horns form a frame for the back of the head. The eyes are deeply drilled, probably to hold an inlay of another material. The head is pierced vertically for suspension. The seal impression shows three animals, two of which are horned. The simplicity of this representation is characteristic of amulet-seals of around 3000 B.C.

Calcite; Mesopotamia or Iran; Jemdet Nasr period (ca. 3000 B.C.).
Height: 3 cm.　　　　　　　　　　　　　　　　　　　(P. O. H.)

104 Elephant Amulet

The body of this calcite amulet is pierced vertically, and the eyes are small, deep sockets. These sockets retain traces of reddish paste, and this may have been adhesive used to hold the eye inlays. One such eye inlay, of black stone, has been reattached with glue and may be the original.

The elephant's trunk hangs vertically, and the head and ears widen above it without differentiation. The elephant is not a common subject for ancient Near Eastern amulets, and there is no parallel for this example. A lapis lazuli elephant is recorded from Kish, but it does not resemble this one and may not even be an elephant. An elephant is also represented on a Jemdet Nasr cylinder seal; although it is not an accurate representation, it must mean that this animal, if not a familiar one, was known to the Protoliterate artist in southern Mesopotamia. Although elephants did not exist in southern Mesopotamia, the Jemdet Nasr period was one of wide expansion and there is evidence of contact between southern Mesopotamia, Syria and Palestine. This amulet could, therefore, come from any one of these areas. The simplified style of the piece relates it to other Jemdet Nasr amulets from the south of Mesopotamia and Elam.

Calcite; Mesopotamia or Elam; Jemdet Nasr period (ca. 3000 B.C.).
Height: 3.7 cm.

BIBLIOGRAPHY: Metropolitan Museum Exhib. Cat., no. 14. Cf. H. Frankfort, Cylinder Seals (1939) pl. 6 c.   (P. O. H.)

105   Ram Figurine

The animal depicted seems to be a ram judging from the structure of the horns. The body, however, is massive and lacks the characteristic features of any particular animal. The horns, which begin at the snout, are carved in low relief and curve around large oval eyes. The upper part of the legs are shown in low relief and the feet are simple short projections without hooves; there is no tail. A dark inclusion in the stone exists behind the head.

Light color stone; Anatolian (?); neolithic period.
Height: 4 cm.; length: 7 cm.   (O. W. M.)

Standing with hands devoutly clasped against the chest and one foot slightly before the other, a scribe has been represented as a suppliant figure. This statuette was undoubtedly a votive offering in a temple. The sheepskin garment is wrapped around the body and over one shoulder, and the hair is bound up in a bun behind the head. The hollow rectangular base is unusual and may represent a piece of furniture or have enclosed an object of another material which would have been visible through the openings on the sides. However, on an early Sumerian alabaster vase from Uruk there is represented a ceremony where two figures stand on a base similar to ours, which in turn rests on a bull. Perhaps the base in this scene and on the bronze statuette are related and had a ritual meaning, maybe representing a type of shrine. No other Early Dynastic copper figurine with a similar base is known. Moreover, no extant Early Dynastic metal statuette is closely relatable to this example. A stone statue of the king Lamgi-Mari, excavated at Mari in Syria, provides a nearer parallel. The deep eye sockets of our statuette were probably inlaid, a feature that does occur on other Early Dynastic copper figures.

Although the provenance is given as Susa, there is nothing Elamite about the style, and if the piece was indeed found in Iran, it may be that it was carried there in antiquity as loot from Mesopotamia.

Copper; Susa (?), Iran; Early Dynastic III period (ca. 2500 B.C.); height: 20 cm.

BIBLIOGRAPHY: For the similar stone statuette of Lamgi-Mari, see A. Parrot, Le Temple d'Ishtar (Mission Archéologique de Mari, I, 1956) pl. 25; Eva Strommenger, Fünf Jahrtausende Mesopotamien (Munich, 1962), fig. 21, below.   (P.O.H.) (V.E.C.)

The inscription on the figure's right shoulder and arm, and on the base, is in Sumerian and has been translated as follows:

^{d}Nin-é-gal-ra	To Nin-egal (a goddess)	Shoulder and Back	1
Lú-Te. ŠARGADU	Lu-Te. ŠARGADU (a personal name)		2
dub-sar	the scribe		3
dumu Ur-^{d}Nin-URTA	son of Ur-Nin-URTA (a personal name)	Base	1
a-mu-na-ru	has presented (this).		2

The following inscription on the base appears to be another attempt of the scribe to write line 1:

107 Foundation Figurine

Metal sculpture of the Early Dynastic III period is known to us from votive figurines, vessels and foundation figures such as this one. Surmounting a nail-shaped body is the upper part of a figure with a horned head-dress symbolic of divinity. Similar figures excavated at Lagash in southern Mesopotamia were found with stone tablets that have inscriptions in the name of Entemena, a king of Lagash in the second half of the 3rd millennium B.C. It is a god, not a king, however, who is represented here with hands clasped, eyes somewhat protruding, a strong arched nose and long hair that hangs down the back in vertical waves. The stone tablets found with the Lagash foundation figures were pierced in the center with a hole and would have been placed over the figures' heads to rest on their shoulders. Cast by the lost wax method, such Early Dynastic III statuettes are invariably made of copper rather than bronze. Foundation figures continued to be made in later times, but their form differed. The closest to this early type are the Neo-Sumerian examples, in which a half figure with arms raised and hands holding a basket resting on its head, ends in a bulging nail-like form. The figure represented in these is the Neo-Sumerian king who was himself divine. Such later works, however, cannot be confused with the Early Dynastic examples, since they differ considerably in form and style. The gesture of the hands, as well as the features of the face and the arrangement of the hair, are all details which place this foundation figurine in the Early Dynastic III period and no later.

Copper; Southern Mesopotamia; Early Dynastic III period (24th century B.C.); Height: 28 cm.

BIBLIOGRAPHY: Cf. E. D. Van Buren, Foundation Figurines and Offerings (Berlin, 1931) pl. 3, figs. 4–6; A. Parrot, Tello (1948) pl. 8., fig. 25 (showing the position of stone tablet on a similar foundation figurine); Richard Ellis, Foundation Deposits in Ancient Mesopotamia (New Haven, 1968); Donald Hansen, "al Hiba, 1968–1969, A Preliminary Report," Artibus Asiae 32 (1972), 246 ff., figs. 8–12.

(P. O. H.)

108   Vessel with Relief

Around this thick-walled periform-shaped vessel is represented a bull in full profile walking to the right. His body, four legs, tail and sex are depicted in relief; details – eyes, leg and body markings – are incised.

The vessel originally had a neck, now broken away. The round base is small and the vessel cannot stand without a support. In the early Sumerian period there was a preference for stone relief vessels such as this one.

Green stone; Sumerian, Jemdet Nasr period, ca. 3000 B.C.
Extant height: 5.6 cm.; diameter: 3.5 cm.

BIBLIOGRAPHY: Cf. W. Nagel, "Frühe Grossplastik...", BJV 6 (1966), pl. IX, 3–5, pl. XI, 1, 3.   (O. W. M.)

109   Foundation Figurine (?)

A nude male kneels on a plinth. One knee is placed under his body while the other rests against his chest. The man holds in both hands an amorphous object lying on the plinth. His eyes are oval and lack eyebrows, his nose is large and thick, and his mouth is a slit. Ears are simple swellings and hair is not articulated. His back is not modeled. A swelling around his neck may represent a necklace.

Below the plinth is a tapering rectangular shank terminating in a point. The whole unit of man and shank were cast in one piece. The object seems to have been designed to serve as a foundation figurine and was probably stuck onto a brick of an important building. Perhaps the object the man holds, or is actually making, is a brick, symbolically used in the construction of the building.

Bronze; Mesopotamian; probably 3rd millennium B.C.
Length: 12.5 cm.; height of man: 4.8 cm.

BIBLIOGRAPHY: Cf. Richard Ellis, Foundation Deposits in Ancient Mesopotamia (New Haven, 1968).   (O. W. M.)

109 bis   Pin with Erotic Scene

The top of this otherwise plain, tapering pin consists of a male and female, both nude and in the round, engaged in sexual embrace and kissing, mouth to mouth. The arms and upper parts of their bodies are free standing, suggesting that the object was made by the lost wax process. The smaller figure, the male, is depicted crouching — the soles of his feet are visible directly below bare buttocks — between the legs of his partner, whose shoulders he claspes; fingers are deliniated. This figure has relatively large ears, slightly raised oval eyes with a shallow depression for the pupil (only the left eye now exists), a sharp, relatively large nose that blends into the features of his partner, and a narrow groove at the forehead, creating a ridge below that might be a fillet. The head is round, button-like, and hair lines are not visible.

The larger figure, the female, grasps the male with her legs, and her arms are around his waist; fingers are delineated. This figure is distinguished by a large, sharp nose in the round, and deep eye sockets, probably once filled with inlays. A shallow groove also exists at the forehead and her head is narrower and less round than that of the male; hair lines are not visible. At the back, just below the head, and not present on the smaller figure, is a clearly raised area that could be back muscles, but which could certainly represent long hair; no decoration is visible. If the pin was meant to be viewed in an upright position, the larger figure is seated; if meant to be viewed tilted (only to the left makes sense), the larger figure is at the bottom. In either case the larger figure must be the female, albeit the un-

feminine face and larger size. The raised area at the back, possibly to be interpreted as hair, lends support to this assumption. Certainly the sexual dynamics of the position would preclude comfortable coitus if one assumes that the larger figure is the male. Indeed, one might theorize that the larger male is merely cuddling the female, that serious love-making has not yet occurred, or was not even intended, but I believe this idea involves us in poetic speculations rather than with the iconographic details present.

If, then, the conclusion that the larger figure is the female is a viable one, it may very well be that her prominence suggests that she is a goddess, and thus the male would then be either a less prominent deity or an especially honored human (no divine attributes are evident for either figure). And perhaps it might be suggested that we have a representation of the well known Sacred Marriage between the king, representing Dumuzi, and the goddess of love Inanna. One may speculate even further that this pin might have been worn on the marriage gown used in the annual ceremony.

In the ancient Near East various sexual positions are depicted in art. Often the male is exhibited making love to the female from behind, but there are also many examples — more than is apparently realized — of face to face love-making. In the latter cases, the female may be seated — apparently the position of the female on our pin — as, for example, exhibited on a terracotta plaque from the Old Babylonian period at Nippur, and on earlier Early Dynastic sealings from Ur. Sometimes the female is shown lying prone, on her back and mounted by the male, in a conventional position, as on Early Dynastic sealings from Ur; or she may be lying on a post or pedestal, as seen on lead plaques from Assur. On some representations both partners appear to be standing, as seen on terracotta plaques from Kish (although it might be that a couch or bed is assumed but not depicted). And sometimes both lovers are shown lying side by side, caressing one another in an apparent pre-coital position, as seen on lead plaques from Assur, and on terracotta plaques from other sites. However, there seem to be no published examples of erotic scenes on pins. And, significantly, only one other example of a loving couple kissing mouth to mouth is known to me. It occurs on the back of a Jemdet Nasr type stone seal from Susa, where a crudely represented couple embrace. Compared to this piece, the Schimmel pin is distinguished by exceptional sensitivity.

In other respects the Schimmel pin reminds us of the pin from Tello that depicts two nude dancing girls in the round, and which may also be erotic in intent. In any event, this pin has the same function as ours in that the top is used to represent a particular scene, a feature that continued all over the Near East for many centuries. The Schimmel pin, as suggested by the faces, might have been made sometime in the third millennium B.C., probably in pre-Sargonid times.

Copper; Mesopotamian or Elamite; 3rd millennium B.C.
Total height: 13.2 cm.; height of female: 3.2 cm.

BIBLIOGRAPHY: Cf. D. McGowan, et al, Nippur I (Chicago, 1967), pl. 137, nos. 4, 7; L. L. Legrain, Ur Excavations III (London, 1936) pl. 18, nos. 365—368; pl. 20, no. 385; H. de Genouillac, Kich II (Paris, 1925), pl. VII, 2, 6; idem., Fouilles de Telloh (Paris, 1934) 46, pl. 10, nos. 2—5; W. Andrae, Die jüngeren Ischtar-Tempel von Assur (Leipzig, 1935), pl. 45; H. Heinrich, Fara (Berlin, 1931), pl. 74, c; MMA de Perse XXV (Paris, 1934), p. 185, fig. 13; cf. P. Amiet, Elam (Auvers-sur-Oise, 1966), pp. 88 f.; see also Robert D. Biggs, SA.ZI.GA Ancient Mesopotamian Potency Texts (Locust Valley, N. Y. 1967). (O. W. M.)

110 Vessel on a Recumbent Bull

The bull has all four legs tucked under its body. They are represented in relief on both sides of the body and at the bottom. The tail is also represented in relief and tucked under the body. The head is at right angles to the body; the horns and ears are quite small. Eyes are depicted on the sides of the head below heavy brows. A vessel, slightly oval when seen from above, rests on the back of the bull. The whole unit is carved in one piece. A dried substance still exists in the vessel.

Limestone; Sumerian; Jemdet Nasr Period, ca. 3000 B.C.
Height: 5.8 cm.; greatest width: 4 cm.

BIBLIOGRAPHY: Cf. Edith Porada, Queens College Exhib. Cat., 26, fig. 3, Ternbach collection; cf. Eva Strommenger, Fünf Jahrtausende Mesopotamien (Munich, 1962), pl. 35, middle and bottom. Cf. R. C. Haines, "The Temple of Iananna at Nippur...," ILN, Sept. 1, 1961, 410, fig. 15.
(O. W. M.)

111 Mace Head

Two recumbent bulls with legs tucked under their bodies, lying side by side on an incised ground line and facing in opposite directions, are carved partly in the round on top of a pear-shaped mace head.
The object was probably used only ceremonially as the perforation for a handle is quite narrow, and the sculpture would preclude the use of the object for striking an enemy.
A similar mace – but with the bulls placed in an opposite direction than ours — is in the F. Cleveland Morgan collection. The motif also occurs on the back of Sumerian stamp seals.

Limestone; Sumerian; probably Jemdet Nasr period, ca. 3000 B.C.
Height: 10 cm.; greatest width: 8.8 cm.

BIBLIOGRAPHY: Fogg Museum Exhib. Cat., pl. XVI, 54; see also H. Frankfort, et. al., Tell Asmar and Khafaje (Chicago, 1932), OIC 13, 110 f., fig. 54; H. Frankfort, "Early Dynastic Sculptured Mace-heads," Analecta Orientalia 12 (1935), 105 ff. (O. W. M.)

112   Head of a Female

The solid modeled head is preserved up to the neck, where it is now broken. Parts of the clay on the face have broken away and the left eye is damaged, but the features are still distinguishable. The face is fleshy and naturalistically rendered. The right eye preserves the eyelid but no pupil is visible; the nose is sharp and of normal proportions; the damaged mouth has a slight horizontal curve and seems to smile slightly. Ears are represented naturalistically in relief and project through the hair at the sides. Seven plain bands are represented in relief around the neck and apparently are a multi-stranded necklace. The hair is thick and shoulder length. A braided band encircles the head and divides the hair in two parts. Incised herring-bone designs represent the hair on the crown, on the side curls, and on the braid; incised lozenge patterns decorate the lower parts of the hair. No traces of paint are extant.

Terracotta; Mesopotamian; late 3rd-early 2nd millennium B.C.
Width: 12.8 cm.; preserved height: 18 cm.

Bibliography: Cf. Eva Strommenger, Fünf Jahrtausende Mesopotamien (Munich, 1962), figs. 141, 167, 168, right; pls. XXII, XXIII; M. T. Barrelet, Figurines et Reliefs en Terre Cuite de la Mésopotamie Antique (Paris, 1968), 72 ff., 362, no. 701.

(O. W. M.)

113 Winged Sphinx

This is a fragment of a female sphinx en face. Her hair is depicted in chunky sections, and her eyes are oval, tapering to the outside, and with a drilled hole for the pupil; ears are visible and depicted in side view. She wears a large collar decorated in zones. The back is smooth and there is no indication of scoring. Sphinxes of exactly the same type are known at Arslan Tash in Syria, and at Nimrud and Khorsabad in Assyria.

Ivory; ca. 9th–8th century B.C.
Preserved height: 5.5 cm.; greatest width: 4.4 cm.

BIBLIOGRAPHY: Cf. F. Thureau-Dangin et al, Arslan Tash (Paris, 1931), pls. XXXI, 32, 33, 34. G. Loud, C. B. Altman, Khorsabad II (Chicago, 1938), pls. 52–54, nos. 42–56; Max Mallowan, Nimrud and its Remains II (New York, 1966), 529, 560, fig. 442, and plate IX. (O. W. M.)

114 Plaque with Cow and suckling Calf

Ivory plaques such as the one illustrated here were placed in metal frames which served as a backing when they were set into the furniture which they decorated. A date in the 9th century B.C. is suggested by comparison with similar ivories found at Arslan Tash, Samaria, Khorsabad and Nimrud. Although to our eye the ivory surface itself is beautiful, it is likely that it was originally covered, at least in part, with gold leaf. A touch of glass paste inlay remains in the calf's eye, and the cow's eye would have been similariy inlaid. In the end, the effect would have been rich and colorful, but perhaps not as subtly beautiful as the unadorned ivory is today.

Ivory; Arslan Tash, Syria; 9th century B.C.
Height: 6 cm.; length: 10.2 cm.

BIBLIOGRAPHY: Cf. S. Thureau-Dangin, Arslan-Tash (Paris, 1931) 135 f., pls. 41–42. (P. O. H.)

115 Plaque with Griffin

Tang on upper edge of frame for attachment to a piece of furniture. The striated form of wing feathers and chevron skirt are features which prove the piece to be of the 1st millennium but do not identify it as the work of any single ivory carving center. This ivory plaque could have been found either at an Assyrian capital or in Syria. Where the piece comes from matters very little since it is surely not Assyrian but Phoenician in workmanship. The position of one wing over the head of the griffin, rather than over his back, is unusual: a small fragment in the Louvre, with a combat between a bull and a griffin similarly has the wing as a background behind the fantastic animal's head, but the scene is otherwise very different.

The upthrown head (which is the characteristic pose for a griffin), the open beak, long head curls and short raised head feathers, make this beast one of the most graceful and attractive of those represented on such ivories.

Ivory; Phoenician; ca. 8th century B.C.
Height: 8.5 cm.; length: 7.2 cm.

BIBLIOGRAPHY: Jewish Museum Exhib. Cat., no. 27. Cf. R. D. Barnett, The Nimrud Ivories (London, 1957), pl. 9; C. Decamps de Mertzenfeld, Inventaire Commente des Ivoires Phéniciens (Paris, 1954), no. 1072.   (P. O. H.)

116 Male Head

This fragment of a cast bronze head is concave in section and perhaps was originally an inlay into a complete statuette of another material. Or it may be all that remains of a hollow-cast bronze figure. The moustache with long downward-curving ends and the beard made up of rows of tight curls followed by an open uncurled area (of which only a piece remains) are of a type that became popular under the Assyrian kings of the 1st millennium B.C. The gentle upward curve of the beard across the cheek before curving downward to meet the moustache is close to the beards of the Assyrians represented on reliefs of the 9th and 8th centuries B.C. Later, the line becomes a downward curve, broken by a sharp angle where it drops more steeply to the moustache. An unusual feature of this head is the line of tight curls which originally also crossed the forehead. Although parallels for this hair style exist in Assyrian art, it is more usual for the forehead hair to be represented by a series of scalloped waves.

In spite of its smallness, the head is a sensitive portrayal of an Assyrian.

Bronze; Assyrian; 9th or early 8th century B.C.
Height: 4.5 cm.

(C. K. W.)

117 Male Statuette

Of the many figurines from the region of Palestine and Syria, this one is most similar to a large group found in a deposit at Byblos in Lebanon. Because this deposit was outside the temple excavated, its date is somewhat in question, but it probably is of the early 19th century B.C. Typical of these figurines are the flattened elongated bodies, the stick-like legs, the tall caps and the gold foil covering the entire surface (here only partially preserved).

The history of Byblos is tied closely to that of Egypt, and the objects found there clearly reflect this influence. The pose of this figurine, as well as its crown, are Egyptian in inspiration. The bent left arm undoubtedly once held a weapon or symbolic attribute.

Bronze; Byblos (?), Lebanon; early 2nd mill. B.C.
Height: 10.7 cm.

BIBLIOGRAPHY: Cf. M. Dunand, Fouilles de Byblos I (Paris, 1939), pl. 58. Cf. A. Schaeffer, Stratigraphie Comparée (1948), 61.

(P. O. H.)

118   Vase with Lion Heads

The extremely soft limestone has been carved into a tall vase with a sharply carinated body and two erect pointed handles. Between the handles are two lion heads facing in. The unusual and distinctive shape of this vase is similar to vessels from Kültepe, in Anatolia, but the 19th century B.C. date of the Kültepe vessels cannot be suggested for the piece in the Schimmel collection.

The lion heards are certainly not earlier than the early 1st millennium B.C. and are related stylistically to those which decorate a number of small bowls, usually of steatite, for which a ceremonial use has been suggested. The chevrons on the bridge of the nose and the crosshatched form of the mane, the deeply sunk eye sockets and the small ears on top of the head are all details common to these lions and to the steatite lion bowls. This would bring the date of the limestone vessel down to about 800 B.C.

Limestone; said to be from Tanjara, Syria; early 1st millennium B.C.
Height: 26 cm.

BIBLIOGRAPHY: Jewish Museum Exhib. Cat., no. 139. Cf. S. Przeworski, Syria 11 (1930), 133 ff.   (P. O. H.)

119 Statuette of a Warrior

Said to be from Jezzine, in the mountains of Central Lebanon. The figure shows none of the Egyptian influence common in objects from the large cities on the coast of the Mediterranean; it is in a local Syrian style.

The characteristic features are the long oval face and projecting chin, the short beard and the ropelike hair with a central braid hanging down the back. The eyes are large, open sockets, the mouth a straight line and the ears a simple ring. The figure wears a knee-length skirt with an elaborate belt, the ends of which hang down the front of the skirt. There are sandals on the feet. The arms are bent at the elbow and the fists are pierced. Originally, the figure held weapons, perhaps a spear and mace.

There are other figurines of this same type, mostly from Central Lebanon, but none has been found at a controlled excavation. Dates ranging from the early to the late 2nd millennium B.C. are assigned to them.

Henri Seyrig, who had published a group of these pieces, reasonably links them to a cache of five cast bronze figurines with a high percentage of copper, found by Robert Braidwood at Judeidah, in the plain of Antioch. The latter are not of the 2nd millennium B.C., however, as Seyrig believed, but of the early 3rd millennium. On this account, it would seem most likely that the figure represented here is a continuation of this same tradition with minor changes later in the 3rd millennium B.C.

Copper; said to be from Jezzine, Lebanon; mid 3rd millennium B.C.
Height: 41 cm.

BIBLIOGRAPHY: H. Seyrig, Syria 30 (1953) pl. 11, fig. 1; Queens College Exhib. Cat., no. 14; Metropolitan Museum Exhib. Cat., no. 28; Jewish Museum Exhib. Cat., no. 129. Cf. The Pomerance Collection of Ancient Art (Brooklyn, 1966) 22 f., no. 15; H. T. Bossert, Altsyrien (Tübingen, 1951) nos. 607, 608.   (P. O. H.)

120 Figurine

A steatopygous nude female sits with her right leg tucked under her body and her left resting in front, the foot pointed outward. When viewed from below the legs are seen to be differentiated from the body. Her breasts are wide and pendant with no nipples represented; wrinkles of fat cover her belly above a prominent navel.

Her right hand touches her breast while the left rests on her thigh; all fingers are neatly articulated on each hand. The head, slightly bent back, is thick and is joined to a massive neck. A flat, pancake-like object is on the top of her head and could be hair, or a cap, probably the former. A plain pigtail falls from this hair to the right of center at the rear. The eyes are oval, without eyebrows, the nose is fairly prominent, the ears are mere swellings, and there is no mouth.

The figurine is quite close to the published stone examples excavated at Çatal Hüyük in Anatolia. There we find the very same type of female, seated in the same position, and with the same foot positions, pancake hair, pigtail and head form, including the lumpy ears and the absence of a mouth. At Çatal Hüyük, however, both hands usually rest on the breast or on the thighs, and multiple belly wrinkles are apparently not common. Indeed, it seems very probable that the figurine comes from some area in western Anatolia, not necessarily Çatal Hüyük itself.

Green stone; Anatolian; Neolithic; ca. 6th millennium B.C.
Height: 5 cm.; width at base: 4.2 cm.

BIBLIOGRAPHY: Cf. James Mellaart, Çatal Hüyük (New York, 1967), fig. 51; also Mellaart's reports on Çatal Hüyük in Anatolian Studies XII (1962), pl. VIII, b, c; XIII (1963), 94, fig. 30; XIV (1964), 74, fig. 26; K. Pearson, P. Connor, The Dorak Affair (New York, 1968), photograph opposite p. 128.   (O. W. M.)

121 Ring with Animal Protomes

The object is fairly heavy and consists of four animal heads spaced equally around a central ring. Each head is flat on top, with the head and muzzle represented on one level, but curved below. The horns curve out around the top edge of the ring, which forms a low rim over the heads. The horns of two of the heads opposite each other are carved in one manner, as part of the mass of the head, those of the two other heads are each carved differently, but with each horn in full relief. Moreover, each head has a different thickness, 5.3 cm., 4.6 cm., 5.8 cm., and one only 3 cm., measuring from the chin to the top of the muzzle. The different depiction of the horns and the difference in head width, noticeable in at least one case, might indicate that there is more than one type of animal represented. Moreover, three of the animals have eyes raised in relief with small holes for pupils while one animal has hollow eyes. Whether this feature was original or represents ancient repair work is not clear. The mouths are represented by a horizontal groove, nostrils by two small holes over the mouth. The top of the ring is fairly round and smooth and undamaged, but the lower part is either broken or left unfinished, forming a bevel sloping inward. The interior walls of the ring are smooth and slope gently inward from top to bottom.

Just what function this object had is not clear. It could have served as a base for a stand or vessel but this suggestion would not explain the jagged bottom. Perhaps it fit over another unit that formed a stand and itself served as some type of cult figure. The object is said to have come from Anatolia and it gives the impression of being quite early.

Basalt; Anatolian; Neolithic period (?).
Length from one animal's nose to another: 25.2 cm.; height: 8.3 cm.; upper perimeter diameter: ca. 10.5 cm. (O. W. M.)

122 Standard

Two bulls in the round stand side by side on a low, narrow base cast together with a shank. This shank is attached to a separately made, hollow base that is decorated by grooves in the form of lozenges. The bulls' legs are straight and free standing; front and rear legs taper toward each other. Except for slight swellings on the rumps and upper front legs, no body decoration exists. Neither of the pointed heads has eyes or mouth; horns curve out and up, facing forward. A metal bar, probably a yoke, connects the bulls at the back of their heads and is joined to the horns by a false loop.

Animal or animal head standards have a history in the Near East extending over thousands of years. While an exact parallel for the Schimmel standard is not at hand, it seems to be related to Anatolian standards dating to the third millennium B.C., and best known from Alaca Hüyük and Horoztepe.

Copper/Bronze; Anatolian; late third millennium B.C.
Total height: 15 cm.; height of bulls: 3.5 cm.; height of base: 3.2 cm.

BIBLIOGRAPHY: Cf. H. T. Bossert, Altanatolien (Berlin, 1942), 297, 298; Oscar White Muscarella, "Anatolia", BMMA, XXVI, 5 (1968), 195, no. 2.
(O. W. M.)

"Cups and rhyta, silver, gold and (precious) stones
thou hast in the Hatti-Land.
But in no other country hast thou their like . . .
Reverence is paid to thy temple, thy rhyta . . . and
they are cared for scrupulously."
A. Goetze, ANET, p. 397: Prayer to Telepinus

The rhyton (better "Tiergefäss") consists of a stag protome and a round cup section decorated with a frieze in relief. The whole unit was hammered from two pieces of silver, the cup and chest section, and the head section, to which the horns ears, neck band, ears, and lip decoration were added. There is no pouring hole at the animal protome end.

The stag is recumbent with its legs tucked under its body, hooves facing out, and knees slightly projecting. The head and upper body are rendered in an extraordinarily naturalistic manner. The body is plain except for an S-shaped swelling of the shoulders, with a small incised circle at the inner curve, and a raised ?-like design at the lower chest. The head is long and thin with hollow oval eyes that once held inlays, and a prominent front tear duct. A typical triangular forelock on the forehead also once held an inlay. Nostrils are in high relief, with hollows at either side, and the mouth is small, represented by an incised line. Face veins are in relief and the jaw is outlined at both sides by three petal-like ridges, similar to the floral pattern on the flanks of deer on the Alaca Hüyük reliefs. The underpart of the jaw is slightly concave.

Soldered around the neck is a necklace with a seam at the rear; it masks the join of the head and body. The decoration consists of a checkerboard pattern formed by cutout alternate squares into which niello (?) inlays were placed. The horns are partly restored but each was originally an upright horn terminating in three short young tines, and a horizontal curved tine. The ears are straight and face forward. Both ears and horns are hollow and were soldered in place. The stag's body terminates in a cup. A narrow strip of silver with square cut-outs above oval ones was added to the outside of the lip of the cup; niello (?) inlays were added to these cut-outs.

On the right side of the stag is a hollow handle, flat on the outside and curved on the inside. One end is joined to the body where there was a cavity to receive it, the other is attached to the lip by a small rivet on the interior. The handle flares out from the body and forms a loop extending beyond the cup. Below the lip is a frieze executed in relief. Two oval sections of gold containing hieroglyphic signs were inserted into prepared hollows in front of the seated goddess and the god on the stag.

The translation of the hieroglyphs has proved to be a difficult task. One scholar suggests a tentative reading of those near the seated figure to be á-x-tá-s, possibly to be read as Amitta/Anitta. Another scholar, Franz Steinherr, would read the signs as á – s(a) – ta$_8$?? – pi LUGAL?KÖNIG, or simpler as Ástapi König, in apposition or Aštapi-LUGAL, a compound name. Note that Astapi is the Hurrian name for the weather god ZABARA, who is represented at Yazilikaya, no. 33. The same scholar translates the hieroglyphs by the god on the stag as KAR-ta$_8$??, or ^{d}Karzi. ^{d}Karzi appears next to ^{d}Astapi at Yazilikaya, as no. 32.

The scene depicts a religious ceremony. A figure, probably a female, and if so, a goddess, sits on a cross-legged chair ending in animals' feet. The goddess wears a long fringed garment and a high pointed hat with one horn in profile; on her feet she wears sandals whose toes turn up into a loop. Her hair at the rear apparently falls into the back of her garment. Her ears, like those of all the figures in the scene, are represented large, in typical Hittite fashion. She holds a bird of prey, probably a falcon, in her extended left hand, and a small cup in her right. Bracelets are worn on both wrists; they are plain and indistinguishable from those worn by all the other figures in the scene.

A brazier, or incense burner (not, apparently, an altar or table as is usual for such scenes), consisting of a column stand with a mushroom-like top, decorated by cross-hatched lines set in zones, separates her from the rear of a male god standing on a stag. He is bareheaded except for a fillet. His hair is plaited and falls at the rear to a point above his knees, a length that is longer than usual for Hittite males. He wears a belted knee-length, short-sleeved garment, and sandals with turned-up toes, and his feet are separated in the Hittite manner. In his extended left hand he too holds a falcon, and in his right a short curved staff, the Kalmus (lituus).

Three men are shown in side view moving left and facing the deities. They are all dressed alike in knee-length, short-sleeved cloaks placed over a longer garment. This garment ends in a triangular section that reaches the ankles at the rear, and another that falls below the elbows; the outer part of this garment is shown between the legs. All are bareheaded except for thin fillets; and two wear typical sandals. Their hair is combed in the form of a pompadour in front and falls back at the rear into their cloaks; straight hair is neatly rendered by incised lines.

The first man holds in his right hand a spouted vessel, a "Schnabelkanne," from which he pours liquid onto the ground; his left hand is held up in a typical Hittite greeting gesture, a clenched fist with the thumb extended. The second man holds what seems to be a tambourine (rather, I suggest, than a loaf of sacred bread?) in both hands and is apparently striking it. The third man kneels on one knee and holds near the base a short spouted vessel in his right hand while his left is held up in a clenched fist like the first man.

Behind the men is a tree or plant consisting of a central unit of four elliptical sections from which curve out three branches on each side. Resting against this tree is a stag tightly curled up with its head turned back toward its body, and apparently dead. Its nose, horns, and jaw are executed in the same style as the stag protome; its body hair is depicted by short incised lines. Above the stag, hanging in space, is a quiver with arrows and shoulder strap, apparently partly covered with a cloth (?), and an object that may be a canteen or bag, perhaps made of leather. Two vertical spears, points down, separate the stag from the seated goddess.

Until the frieze is further studied by experts no definitive conclusions concerning an interpretation can be stated. Nevertheless, some tentative comments about the relationship of the frieze to Hittite art and culture may be brought forth.

Hittite art is basically religious and political. Cult scenes or religious processions are quite commonly represented on the rock reliefs at Yazilikaya, Alaca Hüyük, Giavurkalesi, Malatya, and Fraktin, on terracotta relief sherds, and on many seals. In this respect the Schimmel rhyton frieze fits neatly into a typically Hittite convention and is not surprising.

Free standing spears do not occur on monumental Hittite art, but they do occur, in pairs, and with their points down, on several seals, viz., on a seal in the British Museum (17804) and on another in Dresden. Of interest here is that on both these seals the spears are juxtaposed to a tree. Trees and plants are rare in Hittite art (although not in the later Neo-Hittite period) aside from seals. They do occur on the Alaca Hüyük reliefs, however, and there connected with a stag hunt.

In Hittite texts trees and plants are mentioned in association with rituals and festivals. Spears are mentioned in the texts as objects to be venerated, or as objects upon which the king breaks the sacred loaves of bread. Both gold and silver spears are mentioned, and it may be assumed that those on the frieze actually represent silver examples and are religiously charged. It is possible to interpret that the spears, stag, and tree represent one unit on the rhyton. The existence of the quiver and canteen suggest that the stag was killed in a hunt; perhaps it is being dedicated to the Stag God. Stag hunts are represented in Hittite art at Alaca Hüyük, and on the Selemli (Schimmel) and Alishar Hüyük relief sherds, and on some seals. On the other hand, it is also possible to recognize that the stag and tree form one unit, the spears another. Thus, whether the spears initiate or terminate the scene will not be clear until we are able to interpret correctly their intended position on the frieze. The seated goddess with the cup and falcon has counterparts represented on earlier Kültepe seals. The same goddess is also represented on Hittite seals, viz., on a five-sided seal in Oxford and on the British Museum and Dresden seals mentioned above. (On these seals the wings of the bird are represented open, in a flying position; could they actually represent another bird – a dove?) Subject

to a more refined translation of the hieroglyphs, and to more discussion of the iconography of the seated goddess with a falcon, one finds it difficult to assign a definite name to the seated figure. (Moreover, ᵈAstapi is a male name and if this is confirmed the figure is a god rather than a goddess). Note, however, that the Phrygian Kybele also holds a falcon and a vessel.

A brazier, of a different type than represented here, occurs on a seal from Kültepe, and on some seals found at Tchoga Zanbil in Iran, where religious scenes are depicted; none have, however, hitherto been recognized in Hittite art. That they had some ritual role seems further indicated by their occurrence before a deity on Babylonian Kudurrus (viz., Meli-Shipak II). One also finds them on the famous garden relief of Ashurbanipal of Assyria, and on reliefs from Persepolis, but where kings rather than gods are illustrated.

A god on a stag also occurs on the earlier Kültepe seals. In Hittite art they may be seen together on a small plaque from Yeniköy, near Alaca Hüyük, on the Malatya, and, apparently, on the Haci Bebekli, reliefs, as well as on seals. A rock relief with a god on a stag, from near Birecik, may, as Burney claimed, be neo-Hittite. In addition, an important and relevant text from Boğazköy gives a full description of a statuette (presumably – but no size is given) of a deity made for the town of Viyanavanta. We are informed that the statuette was made of gold and that a god stood on a stag. In this text the god is called "the god who protects the field"; on other texts mentioning this god he is called the "Protective Deity" (Schutzgott); his Luwian name is Runda (Uruwanda). There can be no doubt that our Stag God is the deity described in the Viyanavanta text.

The three men before the Stag God are obviously paying homage and libating to the deities they face. Who they are is not clear, but if one is a king he is not distinguished by dress or appearance. Liquid poured on the ground no doubt guaranteed that only the gods would drink the offering, perhaps wine, beer, oil, or honey, or mixtures of these. On the Alaca Hüyük and Malatya reliefs, and perhaps also at Fraktin, and also on several seals, including some mentioned above, liquid is depicted being poured directly onto the ground.

The clothing of the men is the same as that worn by the man on the "Tarkodemos" seal, now in the Walters Art Gallery, and of disputed date, on men on the Alaca Hüyük reliefs, and on the Bitik and Karahüyük relief sherds. Of interest is the depiction of the rear part of the cloak between the legs, which is rare but occurs on the "Tarkodemos" seal and on the relief of Tudhaliyas found at Alalakh.

Tambourines are both represented in art and mentioned often in religious texts. We see them on the relief sherds from Bitik, Alishar Hüyük, Kaybakli, and Boğazköy, where they no doubt accompanied singing or marching. (Cf. also the later examples at Zincirli and Karatepe.)

Kneeling is also often mentioned in texts, but hitherto one noticed it in Hittite art only in hunting scenes, or practiced by birdmen represented on seals. On some Kültepe seals we do see it practiced

by worshippers. The Schnabelkanne vessel held by the first man was manufactured over a long period of time and was commonly employed for libations; the second vessel is a less common shape. Holding the vessel by the base seems to be a Hittite feature (but is depicted in Sumerian art) and we find it represented on several seals, viz., the Tyszkiewicz seal and another in the Louvre (927). Rhyta, in the form of whole animals or cup types, with or without pouring holes, have been excavated in Anatolia at sites dating from the early second millennium through the Hittite period. All of these examples are made of terracotta, and up to the present no examples of metal have been reported. Nevertheless, rhyta of metal have not been unexpected, for a great deal of information about such objects exists from the many references to them in the texts. Rarely, in fact, does the archaeologist have in hand an object, of which descriptions are common in contemporary texts. We are informed that the gods owned rhyta made of gold, silver, stone, and wood, many of which held inlays, and that rhyta existed in the form of the god's particular animal attribute. There were festivals to rhyta and they were often used in religious ceremonies. They were also given as gifts: we read of a gift sent from Suppiluliumas I to an Egyptian pharaoh:

"...one BIBRU (rhyton) vessel of silver in the shape of a stag, five minas in weight, another in the shape of a ram, three minas in weight".

Rhyta are also represented in art, as on the Tyszkiewicz seal and on a bronze strip from Boğazköy. There can be little doubt but that the Schimmel stag rhyton was the personal property of the Protective Deity, the Stag God, the very same god represented in the frieze.

Dating the rhyton must await further research as there is still disagreement about dating such well known reliefs as those from Yaziliyaka and Alaca Hüyük. Indeed, the frieze on the rhyton is surely related typologically to the relief sherds. Yet, technically the execution of the rhyton frieze is quite superior to those known in terracotta. Moreover, the dating of the relief sherds is still uncertain, and it seems that they were made over a long period of time. Also, motifs continued for a long time in Hittite culture, and thus the rhyton need not be contemporary to the possibly earlier relief sherds. If indeed the Yazilikaya and Alaca Hüyük reliefs are of the Empire period, ca. 13th century B.C., and if the superb workmanship of the rhyton frieze yields a clue one could tentatively accept a ca. 14th–13th century B.C. date for the manufacture of the rhyton (cf. also the bull rhyton). No. 124.

Silver; Hittite; Empire Period, ca. 1400–1200 B.C.
Total length: 17 cm.; total height: 18 cm. Length of stag's body: 12.5 cm.; diameter of the cup: 6.5 cm.; height of frieze: 4.5 cm.; weight, compromised by wax used in restoration: 322.5 grams.

BIBLIOGRAPHY: Cf. Ekrem Akurgal, The Art of the Hittites (New York, 1962), passim, 40 ff., 77 ff., 117, figures 1 f., 19, 47, 52, 76 ff., 92 ff., 99 ff., 101, 104; Kurt Bittel, Hattusha (New York, 1970), 3, 57, 118 f.; H. T. Bossert, Altanatolien (Berlin, 1942), 505, 513, 514, 516, 518 f., 521 f., 527, 550 ff., 570, 594, 596, 634, 692 ff., 715, 775, 817; O. Carruba, "Rhyta in den Hethitischen Texten," Kadmos VI (1967), 88 ff.; A. Goetze, Kleinasien (Munich, 1957), 134, 141 f., 164, 166, 168; in J. Pritchard, Ancient Near Eastern Texts (Princeton, 1955), 208, 210, 348 f., 350, 352 f., 357 ff., 397, 399; O. R. Gurney, The Hittites (Penguin Books, 1952), 127 f., 137 f., 150, 153 f.; H. Güterbock, "Hethitische Götterdarstellungen und Götternamen," Belleten 7 (1943), 295 ff., 314 f.; N. Özgüç, The Anatolian Group of Cylinder Seal Impressions from Kültepe (Ankara, 1965), 15, 56, 61 f., 66 f., 69 f.; Liane Rost, "Zu den Hethitischen Bildbeschreibungen," Mitt. der Instit. für Orientforschung 8, 2 (1961), 161 ff.; J. V. Canby "Tesup" Figurines and Anatolian Art of the Second Millennium B.C., Ph. D. Dissertation (Bryn Mawr, 1959); Sedat Alp, "Die Libationsgefäße Schnabelkanne und Armförmiges Gerät und ihre Hethitischen Bezeichnungen", Belleten 31, No. 124 (1967), 531 ff., R. M. Boehmer, Die Kleinfunde von Boğazköy (Berlin, 1972), 6 B, pl. IX, 169.

Note: It was claimed in 1964, when the objects were acquired, that the stag rhyton, the bull rhyton (No. 124), the seated goddess (No. 125), the bracelet (No. 126), the two spherical headed pins (No. 127), and two ingots (No. 128), one of which was lost, were all found together.   (O. W. M.)

124 Bull Rhyton

The lip and part of the cup, the handle, and parts of the horns have been restored. The body was separately made and added to the head section by being slipped into the head cavity; the join is masked by a grooved collar. The upper parts of the legs, the horizontal parts, as well as ears and horns, and a handle were all separately added.

The angle between the head and cup is not so prominent as that of the stag rhyton. There is no pouring hole at the animal protome end. Repoussé musculature decorates the body above the legs and shoulder and the chest has a sharp dewlap in front with horizontal grooves that indicate the folds of skin. This area is framed by vertical swellings that connect the collar to curved swellings above the legs; this latter feature exists also on the stag rhyton. The legs, horns, and ears are hollow.

The head with its short neck is massive but not clumsy. Oval eyes, and curved sections above and below, the brows, once held inlays. Surprisingly, there is no triangular forelock. The nose is sculpted in the same sensitive manner as on the stag rhyton, but here there is no veining. Also, similar to those on the stag rhyton, are the floral-like patterns on the cheeks. A hump on the back indicates that the bull is a zebu.

Although the bull rhyton is larger than the stag rhyton, the execution and modeling and the use of inlays indicate that these vessels are stylistically related. Of course, we do not know if the bull rhyton originally had a frieze as that part of the cup was destroyed.

The hump at the back of the neck, the horizontal grooving of the dewlap area, with its vertical border, and the type of musculature and cheek decoration are neatly paralleled on other examples of Hittite bulls dating to about 1300 B.C. Surely these examples supply us with a clue for dating the bull rhyton. Considering that the gods owned their own rhyta, made in the form of their attributions, it would seem plausible to assume that the rhyton was the property of the storm god.

Silver; Hittite; Empire Period, ca. 1400–1200 B.C.
Height from knee to top of head: ca. 18 cm.; greatest width: ca. 9 cm.

BIBLIOGRAPHY: Cf. Helene J. Kantor, "A 'Syro-Hittite' Treasure in the Oriental Institute Museum," JNES 16,3 (1957), 148 ff., figs. 3,6,7; F. Fischer, Die Hethitische Keramik von Boğazköy (Berlin, 1963), pl. 133, No. 1278, pl. 135, No. 1280.

(O. W. M.)

A female wearing a plain, high-necked gown that reaches to her ankles, its long sleeves decorated by a double seam or border, sits on a chair and holds a child on her lap. The tips of both her feet barely project from beneath the gown. Her face is fleshy and round, her eyes oval and outlined; eyebrows are raised and join the sharp, straight nose with fleshy nostrils; the mouth is thin with wrinkles at the sides; no ears are visible. She wears earrings made from simple loops, a plain wire necklace, and a loop on each shoulder, all of which are soldered in place. Her headdress consists of a nearly round plain disc (2.2 cm. x 2 cm.) that looks like a disc from the front and back but like a cowl from the sides. A small grooved loop is soldered at the back of the disc for suspension. Hair is depicted at the rear by incised vertical lines decorated in between by lozenge patterns.

Her right hand is extended with the fingers pointing upward. On the surfaces of the finger tips are traces of solder indicating that she once held an object, perhaps a dish. Her left hand is placed adjacent to the child seated on her lap. The child, cast from solid gold, and separately added, is nude, but it is not clear what its sex is; a triangular section in very low relief is marked off and presumably is meant to designate a female, but this is not certain. The head and face are remarkably sculpted for so small a figure (1.5 cm. in height). The head is bald (not contradicting a female attribution), the oval eyes and the ears are relatively large, the nose is small, and there is no mouth. Both the child's hands are clasped together before the chest.

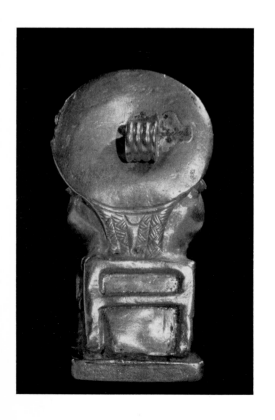

The chair has no back support and is divided into two sections. The lower has four plain legs – the rear ones straight, the front ones curved – ending in typical Hittite lion paws. The upper section duplicates the lower, with the lion paws resting on the horizontal bar in front and joining it at the rear.

The unit rests on a separately made rectangular, hollow plinth. On each side of the chair there is a small metal projection, which can only be the remains of chaplets used in the lost-wax process, the technique used to manufacture the figurine. X-rays show that the interior is hollow, the hands and feet solid, and there seem to be remains of a non-metallic core within.

A very close parallel to our figurine, both in form and material, is said to have been found at Çiftlik, near Kululu; its height is 1.85 cm., half that of our figurine. This gold figurine depicts a goddess seated on a backless throne. She wears a long cloak and has a disc headdress and there is a suspension loop at the rear of this disc. We do not know if she originally held a child on her lap.

Another close parallel to the Schimmel figurine, but made of bronze, and larger, 11 cm. in height, was excavated at Alaca Hüyük. A goddess wearing a long cloak and a disc headdress sits on a backless throne. Her arms are broken, making it impossible to know if she originally held a child or object; nor is it clear whether there was once a suspension loop. A similar female is represented in relief on the stone monument at Eflatun Pinar, where the characteristic disc around her head, if little else, is visible. Also, two small gold figurines with suspension loops, and representing walking male Hittite deities, are now in the Louvre and the British Museum. They, plus the other silver figurine in the

Schimmel collection (131), further document the existence of such portable representations of the Hittite gods. Moreover, in addition to the archaeological evidence, there are many Hittite texts, the so-called Bildbeschreibungen texts, which neatly and conveniently describe gold and silver statues or statuettes of the gods; none yet available, however, describes the seated goddess holding a child. Finally, small gold figurines with loops from Mesopotamia, Ras Shamra, and Egypt attest to the widespread use of such objects, which were probably worn around the neck. The Schimmel figurine goddess is certainly the same goddess that is represented at Eflatum Pinar and in the Çiftlik and Alaca Hüyük figurines. It seems probable that the disc represents the sun, and it is therefore possible that we have at hand a representation of the Sun Goddess of Arinna, "Queen of the land of Hatti, Queen of Heaven and Earth," and a major Hittite divinity. And assuming that the child is her own, it would be the Weather God if a male, Mezallas if a female. In any event, the idea of representing in art a mother goddess holding her child goes back in Anatolia to pre-Hittite times, as indicated by a bronze statuette from Horoztepe, and by the lead figurines from Kültepe. Cf. Isis no. 209.

Gold; Hittite; Empire Period, ca. 1400–1200 B.C.
Height: 4.3 cm.; width of chair: 1.7 cm.; plinth: 1 x 6 cm.; weight: 23.2 grams.

BIBLIOGRAPHY: Cf. Hamit Z. Koşay, Alaca Hüyük Kazisi 1937–39, (Ankara, 1951), 24, Al. b. 10, pl. 67, figs. 1 a, b, 2; cf. also pl. 67, fig. 3; S. Doğan, "The Statuette of Çiftlik," Anadolu XIV (1970), 73 ff., pl. 1; H. T. Bossert, Altanatolien (Berlin, 1942), 527, 594, 596; Altsyrien (Tübingen, 1951), 603–604; Jeanny V. Canby, "New Egyptian Jewelry at the Walters Art Gallery," Jour. Amer. Research Center in Egypt VI (1967), 111, pl. 1, 2 a, b; Liane Rost, "Zu den hethitischen Bildbeschreibungen," Mitt. des Inst. für Orientforschung 8, 2 (1961), 175 ff.

(O. W. M.)

126 Bracelet (?)

The object is made from one piece of gold with the edges turned back. There are cuts visible in the rolled edge, made no doubt, to facilitate creating a neat even roll.

If this object was a bracelet, it could only have been used by a small child. It reminds one of a modern napkin ring and may, in fact, have held a royal napkin or towel.

Gold; Hittite; Empire Period, ca. 1400–1200 B.C.
Diameter: 4 cm.; weight: 16.4 grams.

BIBLIOGRAPHY: cf. Helene J. Kantor, "A 'Syro-Hittite' Treasure in the Oriental Institute Museum," JNES 16, 3 (1957), 158, pl. XXV, c.   (O. W. M.)

127 Two Pins with Spherical Heads

Both pins are exactly the same in all details. The head is a slightly flattened hollow sphere with twenty-four grooves or corrugations, the top of which has an eight-petal rosette and a central circle raised in relief. A separately made thin wire collar masks the join where the solid pin was inserted into the sphere. The pin tapers toward the point. Each of the spheres has a loose object within that gives the pin the quality of a rattle when it is shaken.

Gold; Hittite; Empire Period, ca. 1400–1200 B.C.
Length: each pin is 13.3 cm.; diameter of one sphere is 1.9, the other is 2.1 cm.; height of the spheres is 1.4 cm.; weights: 20.9 and 19.6 grams.

BIBLIOGRAPHY: Cf. R. M. Boehmer, Die Kleinfunde von Boğazköy (Berlin, 1972), pl. XVII, 282; pl. XXI, 479; H. H. von der Osten, The Alishar Hüyük, III (Chicago, 1937), pl. 105, d 437; T. Özgüç, "Excavations at Kültepe, 1954," Belleten 19, 73 (1955), 69, figs. 33, 35, 77; P. Jacobsthal, Greek Pins (Oxford, 1956), 37, 138, 139.   (O. W. M.)

128 Ingot

The shape of the ingot is amorphous, and, judging from the evidence of the undamaged edges, may have been so originally. There also indications that pieces of silver were cut off in antiquity, leaving jagged edges.

A silver disc and an amorphous ingot were excavated at Zincirli in North Syria. Both objects were inscribed with the name of the eighth century B.C. king Barrekub. Our ingot is incised with several Hittite hieroglyphs, which are now only slightly visible. Tentatively, Franz Steinherr says that one sign could represent the word for country, another the word for scribe. It is possible, because the ingot was said to have been found together with the silver Hittite rhyta, that it was part of an artisan's repair kit, or that it formed part of his working stock. On the other hand, it is also possible that pieces of silver were cut from the ingot and weighed, to be used as currency.

Silver; Hittite; Empire Period, ca. 1400–1200 B.C.
Extant diameter: 7.8 x 9 cm.; thickness: .5 cm.;
extant weight: 200 grams.

BIBLIOGRAPHY: Cf. F. von Luschan, Die Kleinfunde von Sendschirli (Berlin, 1943), 119 ff., figs. 170, 171; pl. 58 t–v; D. Bivar, "A Hoard of Ingot-Currency of the Median Period from Nush-i-Jan, Near Malayir," Iran IX (1971), 98 ff.   (O. W. M.)

129 Medallion

The medallion has the form of a round disc of gold with a rolled loop for suspension at the top. The disc is decorated in repoussé with a star or sun having eight rays. The center consists of a raised dot surrounded by nine smaller ones; a large raised dot is also placed within each section and smaller ones extend along the outer border. In Anatolia similar medallions in bronze were found in the Hittite cemetery at Gordion; others with a slightly different motif occur at Boğazköy.

Earlier examples of medallions with simple dot designs occur at Horoztepe and at Alaca Hüyük. The motif of a star or sun ray was commonly represented on medallions and stamp seals excavated at many sites all over the Near East, in Palestine, Mesopotamia, and Iran, dating to the second and early first millennia B.C.

Gold; Anatolian; 2nd mellennium B.C.
Diameter: 3.4 x 3.9 cm.; weight: 9.3 grams.

BIBLIOGRAPHY: Cf. Machteld Mellink, A Hittite Cemetery at Gordion (Philadelphia, 1956), 41, pl. 23, h, j; Kurt Bittel, Hans Güterbock, Boğazköy (Berlin, 1935), 33, pls. 11, 22; compare also C. K. Wilkinson, "The Art of the Ancient Near East," BMMA (March, 1949), figure on p. 195; E. L. B. Terrace, The Art of the Ancient Near East in Boston (Boston, 1962), fig. 13. R. M. Boehmer, Die Kleinfunde von Boğazköy (Berlin, 1972), 19 ff.; figs. 5, 11, 12, 13, 16, 17.   (O. W. M.)

130 Lobed Headed Pin

The head and shank are cast in one piece. The head consists of five thick lobes, with a raised dot at the top of each and one at the top center. The shank tapers gently to a point.

Similar pins, made of gold or bronze, were known in Anatolia in the third millennium B.C. and continued to be used into the late second millennium; they occur, for example, at Alaca Hüyük, Boğazköy, Alishar, Kültepe, and Gordion. When found in graves, such pins occupy a position near the shoulder, suggesting that they served as garment fasteners.

Gold; Anatolian; 3rd–2nd millennium B.C.
Length: 8.4 cm.; weight: 10 grams.

BIBLIOGRAPHY: Cf. Remzi O. Arik, Les Fouilles d'Alaca Höyük (Ankara, 1937), pls. 61, 109, 217; Ausgrabungen von Alaca Höyük (Ankara, 1966), pls. 42, 123; Kurt Bittel, Hans Güterbock, Boğazköy (Berlin, 1935), 31 ff., pls. 11, 13; Erich F. Schmidt, The Alishar Hüyük Seasons of 1928 and 1929, I (Chicago, 1932), fig. 202; H. H. von der Osten, The Alishar Hüyük Seasons of 1930–32, II (Chicago, 1937), figs. 136, 282, 284; Tahsin Özgüç, "Excavations at Kültepe 1954," Belleten, 19, 73 (1955), 64 ff., figs. 34, 76, 84, 89; Machteld Mellink, A Hittite Cemetery at Gordion (Philadelphia, 1956), 32 f., pl. 19,o; Paul Jacobsthal, Greek Pins (Oxford, 1956), 154, n. l; R. M. Boehmer, Die Kleinfunde von Boğazköy (Berlin, 1972), 79 ff.   (O. W. M.)

131 Seated Female Figurine

The female wears a high-necked, long-sleeved, ankle-length gown, with wrinkles indicated on both arms. She wears a fillet around unarticulated hair at the crown of her head. At the rear her hair is plaited and rendered in relief, falling to the shoulders, where it joins the remains of a loop for suspension. A plaited band executed in low relief continues down the back to the seat line and presumably is the continuation of her hair. Her ears are typically large, her face round; she has small outlined oval eyes, a sharp nose, thin mouth, and a small round chin. She sits on a narrow chair with raised sides, each having an incised groove from the middle to the base, and a solid rear with no back support. Only one foot, projecting slightly from under the center of her gown, is shown. The whole unit, cast from solid silver, rests on a separately made solid plinth, placed to one side rather than at the center. In her extended right hand she holds a plate (or bread?); the left hand holds a small object, perhaps a cup, against her breast; fingers are not articulated.

A similar figurine was found in 1953 at Kayali Boğaz, quite near to Boğazköy. It is made of gold and is only 2 cm. in height, and the chair is placed in the center of the plinth. However, from the seated position, the gown with wrinkles, the position of the hands, the single foot, the hair style, and the rear loop, it can surely be inferred that the two figurines represent the same goddess.

Silver; Hittite; Empire Period, ca. 1400–1200 B.C.
Height: 3.2 cm.; plinth: 1.6 x 1.8 cm.; weight: 21.9 grams.

BIBLIOGRAPHY: Kurt Bittel, Boğazköy III, Fund aus den Grabungen 1952–1955 (Berlin, 1957), 30 f., pl. 27.   (O. W. M.)

132 Relief Sherds

Four relief sherds with representations of a stag hunt are said to have been found at Selimli, not far from Alaca Hüyük in Turkey; they have been published by Kurt Bittel in the Carl Weickert Festschrift. The sherds belong to a well known and fairly common class of objects dating to the Hittite period, other examples of which have been found at Boğazköy, Yazilikaya, Alishar, Alaca Hüyük, Bitik, Kültepe, Karahüyük, Kabakli, and Inandik, as well as at Selimli. Unfortunately, all of the presently known examples are in the form of fragments as no complete vessel has yet been recovered. The scenes represented are usually concerned with cult activities or processions of people, and animal and hunting scenes; a few scenes are erotic, probably representing events related to a cult.

Reliefs on pottery are of interest not only for their archaeological and artistic value but also because they demonstrate that reliefs were executed not only on rocks. Moreover, they represent the terracotta counterparts of the reliefs represented in metal, as evidenced by the Schimmel stag rhyton. Bittel and Bossert also suggest that relief vessels may indicate the existence of stucco reliefs on temple walls, none of which has yet been recovered. Note also that on the Schimmel stag rhyton a stag apparently killed in a hunt is also depicted.

It is of interest to point out that the triangular markings employed to indicate body hair on the stag continued for some time, as we find the same markings on 8th century Iranian ivories said to have been found at Ziyiye in Iran (viz. Metropolitan Museum of Art, 51.136.5).

The dating of the relief vases is still under discussion, but all authorities believe that the Selimli fragments are late in the series and definitely belong to the Empire period, somewhere between 1400 and 1200 B.C.

Terracotta; Brown clay with a red polished surface; Hittite; ca. 1400–1200 B.C.

BIBLIOGRAPHY: Kurt Bittel, "Eine hethitische Reliefvase aus Kappodokien," Festschrift für Carl Weickert (Berlin, 1955), 24 ff.; Tahsin Özgüç, "The Bitik Vase," Anatolia II (1957) 57 ff.; William Stevenson Smith, Interconnections in the Ancient Near East (New Haven, 1965), 108; F. Fischer, Die hetitische Keramik von Boğazköy (Berlin, 1963), pl. 129.   (O. W. M.)

The belt was repaired and various parts have been restored in recent times. The right border, overlapped by the left, is restored. The shape of the belt seems always to have been round and it is possible that its length was never much greater than it is now. A row of small holes punched from the front extends across the top, bottom, and side edges for attachment to a backing; no buckling apparatus is extant.

One hundred fifty figures were originally arranged by vertical units of five each into thirty registers, taking up almost the entire area of the belt. No filler or dividing ornaments exist between the registers or figures, except for two continuous narrow raised bands at the top, bottom and side edges of the frieze. The intent of the representation is to convey a continuous hunting scene, reproduced vertically five times. Actually, a true vertical alignment is not always achieved, especially in the first nine registers (arbitrarily moving from the right edge to the right, left on the photograph). Nor is there uniformity in the space that separates any two figures, so that overlapping of registers, or of one figure by another, is not uncommon; occasionally the tails of creatures were intertwined (registers 23 and 24; 17 and 18 are restored).

Basically there are five types of figures represented with variations. They are placed irregularly in the sequence of registers and face as follows: *a standing archer* wearing a long-sleeved, fringed tunic extending below the knees, with a wide belt and boots. He holds a bow in his left hand and shoots left at lions and bulls; the bow string does not cross over his body and the narrow shaft is sometimes represented along his forearm. A long quiver with pointed base, divided into panels, is slung across the back (IL). The top archer is missing but would have been situated to the right of his colleague below.

Striding lions: with rear legs together (except for the lowest lion in register 2), one front leg on the ground, the other held up; some turn to look backward. Their open mouths reveal teeth, fangs, and a sharp protruding tongue; an "S" curl exists on the lower lip; the muzzle is wrinkled; an incised "wart" is depicted on the forehead and ear; and the eye is a punched circle. The mane is decorated by short incised strokes; the belly is outlined and decorated with thin incised lines, one time with a herring bone pattern. Shoulders are outlined and the legs decorated by horizontal lines and curved vein lines; a "saddle" motif is placed on the backs. The tail curves upward over the body ending in a conelike motif; the paws are drawn as a series of lumps (2R, 29L).

Bulls charging (or collapsing?): with lowered heads. The rear legs are shown as if walking, the front legs bent and close together; horns project forward, then down and out; eyes are punched circles with a thick brow. Manes extend the length of the back and are represented by short vertical strokes ending in punched circles. "Tassles", vertical strokes ending in punched circles, are pendent from the neck and rump. The belly is outlined by two lines and is decorated either by punched circles or strokes. Chests are usually depicted by short strokes, once by punched circles; sex is not depicted. The tails curve over the body and end thickly with a herring-bone or simple incised design (3L, 18L, 24L, 30R); bulls in register (3 and 5) have arrows sticking in the backs of their necks, except for the lowest ones.

Springing lions: like register 2 in details, but here with rear legs drawn in a walking position and with both front feet raised, one horizontally, one bent (4L); the fourth lion from the top has an arrow in its neck.

Galloping bulls: like 3 in details, but here front and rear legs are together (5R, 7R, 26L); only some of the bulls of 5 have an arrow in their necks.

Chariots: the bodies of both horses are shown as one except for the heads; front legs are raised slightly off the ground; bodies are plain but for harnass decoration and front and rear head plumes. Manes are depicted by framed horizontal strokes. Tails are decorated with simple strokes or herring-bone designs; they curve out and then down gently, narrow, and then flare out. Male sex is represented by a small swelling. A charioteer leans forward from the box holding reins in both hands, and a whip; an archer shoots at the animals backward from the chariot. Both men wear plain, pointed helmets, tunics decorated by vertical and horizontal lines, and apparently a belt. The chariot box has a concave upper and a convex left border, and it is decorated by vertical and horizontal lines; the wheels have six or eight spokes. There is no rear mounted shield or spear, nor a quiver

on the chariot box. The men's features are crudely drawn with square jaws and a mouth depicted by horizontal strokes; the eyes are oval (6R, 13R, 25L); part of the first, fourth, and most of the fifth chariots and horses in registers 13 and 25 are restored.

Striding lions: like other lions in details but here three legs are on the ground and one is raised (8L, 23R).

Galloping bulls: like register 5, but with heads turned back (9R).

Helmeted archers: in a long-sleeved, ankle-length, fringed tunic, shoot backward in the "Parthian shot" manner from galloping horses. The archer's legs are at right angles to his thighs, his face like the chariot riders. The horse's front legs are off the ground and is the same type as the other horses represented; there is no saddle depicted (10R, 15R, 20L); only register 15 is completely preserved.

Charging bull: like the other bulls in details; here one front foot is slightly raised over the other and both rear legs are shown (11L, 16L; 21 and 22L and R). The turned-back heads of the bulls in register 21 are restored, but lions and bulls are depicted together.

Springing lion: like the other lions in details; here both rear legs are together, and one front leg is held up at an angle, the other horizontally (12R, 14R, 17R, 19R, 21L, R, 27R).

Man on a galloping horse: holding the reins in his right hand; a shield is held either in his left hand or is tied to his shoulder, one cannot make out which. The upper two horsemen alone have an object projecting from their shoulders. Whether this is a raised left arm to hold a spear (not drawn) or a type of quiver is not clear. Man and horse are like the others represented (28L).

Thus there are ten registers of lions, eleven of bulls, one showing both, one register of archers, three of chariots, and four of cavalry, three of which have bows, one perhaps with a spear or a quiver.

Each figure is drawn and decorated individually. The bodies of the animals, the chariots and wheels, and sometimes the horsemen, were first hammered from behind in low relief, and then arms, legs, tails, etc., were drawn in with a thin sharp tool, after the body outlines were incised.

A linear rather than a plastic style prevails. Details of drawing and body decoration differ from figure to figure even within the same register. There is also no apparent order as to which figure is attacking which other figure: lions attack bulls, bulls fight back, cavalry (surprisingly with shields) and chariotry attack both lions and bulls. Registers 1 to 15 have five registers moving left, ten right; registers 16 to 30 have nine moving left, five right. A general, but not visually obvious, division of the registers into two zones may be seen in the fact that the chariots and cavalry of registers 6, 10, 13, and 15 face right, whereas those of 20, 25, and 28 face left.

The large number of figures and the particular types of body position and decoration appear to be unparalleled on published Urartian belts and other engraved metal work. At the same time the figures and motifs – galloping position, chariots, hunting scene, etc. – clearly fit into the decorative style and scheme established by Urartian art. Thus the body decoration on the lions' mane, belly, saddle, and paws is comparable to that found on the apparently 7th-century B.C. belt from Guschi and on one from Karmir Blur.

The use of "warts" on the head and ear, and the "S" curl on the lip, seem to relate best to these motifs found on lions from the time of Argisti I (ca. 786–764 B.C.) and Sarduri I (764–753 B.C.). The bull's features, the use of "tassels," the curve of the horns, mane decoration, occur in 8th and apparently also in 7th-century Urartian art, for example from the time of the two above mentioned kings, and also on the Guschi belt and on the Adilcevaz stone relief; also in part on the bulls represented on the shields of Rusa III (ca. 625–610/585 B.C.), especially the chest decoration and the sharp leg joints. Chariots and/or cavalry (but without shields) in scenes depicting hunted bulls and lions, occur in the art of Argisti I and Sarduri II, and also on belts from Nor Aresh, Tli, Altintepe, and Kayalidere (a belt?). On one of the belts from Nor Aresh the chariot box has no rear spear, a chariot archer shoots backward, and there are also supporting cavalry with spears; in addition, bulls and lions, with arrows in their necks, are hunted. Perhaps this belt is the closest in motif to the Schimmel belt. The belt from Tli has an archer standing on the ground, as well as chariots and cavalry, all hunting bulls and lions. The Tli belt, however, is very stylized and appears to be more Caucasian than Urartian in style.

Human features appear to be close to those represented during the time of Argisti I and Sarduri II, especially with respect to the mouth and nose configuration. The "Parthian Shot" motif occurs on a belt in the Ashmolean Museum; it also occurs in Assyrian relief art of the 9th and 7th centuries B.C., in the art of Cyprus, and on a shield from Crete, as well as later in the art of the Sasanian period.

Significantly, this type of shooting is mentioned as an Urartian technique by Sargon II in the report of his eighth campaign which took him to Urartian-controlled areas in 714 B.C.

Dating stray Urartian objects is never easy because little of Urartian art is objectively dated, unless there are inscriptions, and individual details and motifs continued for a long time. It would seem that if belts from Ani Pemsa, Zakim, Tli, Guschi, and those from Karmir Blur do in fact date from the 7th century B.C., because of their use of filler ornaments and sometimes the occurrence of an intricate network dividing the figures from each other, paralleled on some of the objects from Ziwiye in Iran, then our belt, and those from Nor Aresh, Kayalidere, and Altintepe (found in a tomb dated by an inscription to time or Argisti II, ca. 714–685 B.C.), could be earlier. The Schimmel belt might tentatively be dated somewhere between the late 8th and the early 7th century, B.C., perhaps from the late years of Sarduri I through the reign of Argisti II.

Bronze; Urartian; late 8th – early 7th century B.C.
Preserved length: ca. 1 meter; width: 13.8 cm.; diameter: ca. 31 cm.

BIBLIOGRAPHY: Herbert Hoffmann, "An Urartian Decorated Bronze strip from Diyarbakir," in Studies Presented to G.M.A. Hanfmann (Mainz, 1972), 69–76, especially p. 76; cf. R. W. Hamilton, "The Decorated Bronze Strip from Guschi," Anat. Studies XVI (1965) 41–51; Guitty Azarpay, Urartian Art and Artifacts (Berkeley, 1968), 47–50.
(O.W.M.)

25

28

30, 29

20

134 Brooch

A hollow recumbent lion is set into a low rectangular frame. The lion's body is plain except for the head; only a small part of the upper tail is shown in relief. The rear and front legs are in relief but both front paws were added separately.

Around the neck is an incised collar decorated with pairs of evenly spaced lines. The mane above the collar is depicted by incised long curls, the ruff around the jaw by incised triangles.

Four lobelike swellings form the muzzle around the nose, which has two wavy wrinkles. The eyes are large and oval with thick brows. On top of the head is a thick ledge, not quite gable shaped, with two tear shaped plain ears in low relief. Vertical incisions decorate the low front of the ledge.

The mouth is open showing four fangs with no indications that they were added, and an upper row of teeth shown as incisions. A protruding tongue overlaps the lower teeth. A seam is faintly visible on the back and indicates clearly that the lion was made from two pieces joined together.

The sides of the frame were all added and decorated with three milled wires. The base is plain but for three spools at the rear end with a piece of gold wire still in place. At the front end is a damaged area. It would seem that two pins originally were placed here and joined a now missing catch. Thus the object was probably a brooch. The closest parallels appear to be brooches excavated at Ephesus and Sardis, and it may be that our brooch is a product of a Lydian, or maybe an East Greek workshop.

Electrum; Lydian or East Greek (?); ca. 6th century B.C.
Length of Lion: 3.8 cm.; total height: 2.4 cm.; depth of frame: .6 cm.;
frame: 3.2 × 2.1 cm.; weight: 16 grams.

BIBLIOGRAPHY: Cf. C. Densmore Curtis, Sardis, XIII (Rome, 1925) 34, pl. VIII, figs. 7 a, b, c; D. G. Hogarth, Excavations at Ephesus (London, 1908), pl. X, nos. 34, 35, 40, 41.   (O. W. M.)

135 Rhyton: Calf-Head

This grey burnished rhyton is made of a number of separate pieces. The neck is wheel-made and the head moulded. The ears and horns are separately applied. The engraved details were added after moulding. The handle, which is attached to the under surface of the head, gives the rhyton a Greek, rather than Near Eastern, form. The stylization of the animal head and the monochrome grey ware is similar to Phrygian pottery, and it may be that the piece belongs to the late Phrygian period when Greek influence becomes noticeable, in the sixth or fifth century B.C.

Terracotta; Anatolia; 6th – 5th centuries B.C.
Length: 21 cm.; diameter of rim: 9.8 cm.

Bibliography: K. Tuchelt, Tiergefässe in Kopf- und Protomengestalt (Berlin, 1962), pl. 11 (P. O. H.)

Made from two pieces, this complete ladle has a handle that curves twice to imitate a water bird's neck and terminates in an ibis's (?) head. Two round eyes and a triangular cut-out on the top of the head once held inlays.

The handle is attached to the bowl by two rivets. On the outside of the bowl are two incised guilloche bands framed by narrow hatched spaces that cross at right angles and join a similar band at the lip. Where the crossed guilloches meet at the center is a four-petalled rosette within a rhomboid, the whole within concentric circles; the interior of the bowl is plain.

Bronze ladles with upright handles terminating in animal heads were excavated from tumuli at Gordion in Turkey dating to the late 8th century B.C. In Iran a ladle with a curved animal-head handle was found at Hasanlu IV, ninth century B.C. (unpublished); one with a straight handle was excavated at Sialk B, of ninth-eighth century B.C. date; and a couple with long straight handles ending in hooks come from Marlik, about 1000–800 B.C.

Bronze; Iranian; early first millennium B.C.
Length: 19.3 cm.

BIBLIOGRAPHY: Cf. Rodney S. Young, "Gordion on the Royal Road," PAPS 107, 4 (1963), 360 f., and fig 17; Roman Ghirshman, Fouille de Sialk (Paris, 1939), pl. 50, S545 a; Ezat Negahban, A Preliminary Report on Marlik Excavation (Teheran, 1964), figs. 27, 34.   (O.W.M.)

137 Standard

The hollow circular unit with cut-out, curved sections and a short shaft for attachment has six rings around the perimeter and, at the top a couchant ram, whose legs are tucked up under his body. The ram itself is decorated with cut-outs (similar to a ram in the Louvre) and has long sweeping horns. The six rings may have been cast with the round unit, but the ram seems to have been added. In general, such standards are related to those used in Anatolia (Alaca Hüyük) and the Near East from early times. Closer in type however, are several reported to have come from Iran, none of which has been scientifically excavated. A pair of these standards is in The Metropolitan Museum of Art; each consists of a decorated, hollow, round unit with a shaft, on top of which is a walking man flanked on either side by a ram, similar to ours, and a dog.

Another pair, in a private collection, is quite close to the Schimmel standard, in the form of the round unit, the rings on the perimeter, and the central couchant ram, but here there are also a bird and another animal.

Furthermore, two other standards, also a pair, one in the Louvre, the other in Toronto, are clearly related typologically to these. All the standards apparently occur in pairs, and if we knew the circumstances of their provenience, we could better discuss their function. It also seems clear that Elamite art played some role in the origin of these objects, and they all seem to belong to the late second millennium B.C.

Bronze; Iranian, late second millennium B.C.
Height: 18.3 cm.; height of ram: 5.8 cm.; outer diameter of round unit: 11.3 cm.

BIBLIOGRAPHY: First published by Ann Farkas in 'Animal Style' Art from East to West (Asia Society, 1970), frontispiece, 54 f., no. 23. Cf. Prudence Oliver, "Art of the Ancient Near East The Second Millennium B.C.," BMMA (April, 1960), 257, fig. 17; Trésors de l'Ancien Iran (Geneva, 1966), no. 540, fig. 35; Peter Calmeyer, Datierbare Bronzen aus Luristan und Kirmanshah (Berlin, 1969), 50 ff.

(O. W. M.)

138 Quiver Plaque

More than a dozen sheet-metal quiver plaques of similar design and style exist in museums and private collections. Since none has been scientifically excavated, their exact find spots are not known, but they are all thought to have a general western Iranian provenience. Most of the decorated plaques are divided into five panels: the first, third, and fifth are often decorated and the others left plain; occasionally four or even all five panels are decorated; at other times they are all undecorated. Two bronze quivers excavated at Hasanlu (unpublished, 70–662 and 70–670) have three plain panels; and one from War Kabud has six uneven panels decorated with repoussé dots, circles, and rosettes. One of the main characteristics of the decorated quivers is that the execution of the figures is quite crude; sometimes they are only casually incised onto the bronze. The Schimmel quiver is an exception and is quite finely executed. The quiver gently tapers in width from top to bottom (not preserved). A flange, one cm. wide, is bent back from the metal on both sides and each is pierced with small holes their entire length. Eleven small holes exist at the top edge and four larger holes along the left edge. All the holes, except one large one, were punched from the front. The small holes were no doubt needed to join the plaque to a leather or wicker backing; the larger ones probably held shoulder straps.

Panel one has a bearded god in a long dress facing right and drawn to about the knee line. He is placed within a disc with its wings and tail decorated in a feather pattern. The god wears a rectangular hat with a feathered (?) top, reminding us of a Babylonian crown. In his left hand he holds a ring and his right hand is open and raised. Two bearded gods in long cloaks and pointed hats with one pair of horns, and hands raised, stand below. Panels two and four are plain but elaborately framed by a zone of decoration consisting of a mountain motif and what looks like rows of stacked hay. In panel three, a hero holds a snarling lion with turned-back head in each hand. He has four wings and is dressed in a knee-length kilt; he wears a fillet and is barechested and barefooted.

Panel five, partly preserved, has a man holding a spear in his right hand and stabbing a lion. His left hand holds the lion's ear while his left foot rests on its body. The spear appears to pass behind the man only because the shaft was not drawn across his body.

Except for the hero's wings, all the figures are raised from behind in low relief, and all details of clothing design and body motif are incised from the front with a chisel and punching tool. The double lines dividing each panel and the framing borders of the undecorated panels are also raised from behind, but the muntain and hay design is incised.

The closest parallel to this quiver is in the Borowski collection, but individual features also are duplicated on examples in the Feroughi and Bröckelschen collections.

Some of the clothing depicted here is the same as that on some Iranian beakers ("situlae") of the tenth and ninth centuries B.C.

The date of the quiver is probably ninth century B.C., as Calmeyer and Moorey have suggested.

Bronze; Iranian; ca. ninth century B.C.
Greatest length: 54 cm.; upper width: 13.5 cm.; lower width: 9 cm.

BIBLIOGRAPHY: Cf. Peter Calmeyer, Datierbare Bronzen aus Luristan und Kirminshah (Berlin, 1969), 81–87; Altiranische Bronzen der Sammlung Bröckelschen (Berlin, 1964), 43–45; "Kockerbeschlag," in Das Tier in der Kunst Irans (Stuttgart, 1972), 54; P. R. S. Moorey, Catalogue of the Persian Bronzes in the Ashmolean Museum (Oxford, 1971), 254–256.   (O. W. M.)

Fantastic animals of many sorts and varieties were commonly represented in ancient Near Eastern art. Among the favorites was the lion-griffin. In early representations on seals this creature carries weather-gods on his back. Later, on seals and on the great Assyrian stone reliefs of the 9th century B.C., lion-griffins are pursued or attacked by hunters. The significance of this fantastic animal in the ancient East is obscure and must have changed over the millennia. His ferocious appearance could have made him either a protective guardian or a vicious antagonist.

The head illustrated here is essentially that of a lion. Only the tall upright ears give final evidence that this is not a lion but a lion-griffin. The mouth is open in a roar, and the tongue protrudes slightly from the lower jaw. A raised ruff encircles the head below the ears. The head itself is well modelled, the skin bulging realistically above the eyes and rising in wrinkles around the mouth and nose. A small lump protrudes from the center of the forehead, as it does on griffins. The surface decoration is not limited, however, to this feature. The beast's face is covered with incised and punched detail. Tiny circles of dots decorate the cheeks; long lines of dots follow the ridges below and above the nose, and dotted chevrons go up between the eyes. In addition, the triangular eyes have dotted borders as does the mouth. The back of the neck and the ruff are undecorated, but the inner surface of the ears is hatched around the edges. The inside of the mouth is also richly detailed. A central depression runs down the tongue and dots cover its surface. The roof of the mouth has horizontal rows of dots and lines, and the teeth are all carefully deliniated. (The four protruding teeth are restorations.)

The provenance of this handsome bronze is said to be northwest Iran. Certainly in style the piece does not fall into any known category such as Assyrian or Achaemenian. Not enough is yet known of the peoples who inhabited north-western Iran late in the second and early first millennium B.C. to make it possible for us to attach the name of a people or style to this piece. The triangular eye is a feature which is common in Urartian animal heads, but such details as the nose and mouth wrinkles and the dotting of the surface differ entirely from any Urartian work of art known to us at this time.

The manner in which this head was employed must also remain in question. The rim below the repoussé ridge and dotted border is pierced with two pairs of holes, one on either side. There is no sign of wear around these holes, and they cannot have held attachments to support a handle such as those used for situlas. The shape of the face with the right-angle bend of the jaw also makes it unlikely that it was ever intended to be a vessel. Protruding from the backs of Assyrian chariots represented on the Balawat gates are roaring lion heads, symbolic and decorative guardians attached to the vehicles. The perfect condition of the tall ears rivetted onto this head indicates, however, that it was probably never set in a place where it would easily have been harmed or destroyed, and it may, therefore, have been a piece of architectural decoration. The wonderful life and ferocity which still immediately impress the viewer remain as great as when the head was made.

Bronze; N.W. Iran; early 1st mill. B.C. Length: 20 cm.; diameter (rim): 13 cm.

BIBLIOGRAPHY: Museum of Fine Arts, Boston, *Bulletin*, 331 (1965), pl. 5; cf. The Pomerance Collection of Ancient Art (Brooklyn, 1966), 41, no. 47.   (C. K. W.)

140 Bowl

The shallow bowl narrows toward the base and is thick walled. A stylized ram's head protome projects from one side; it has no eyes, mouth or nostrils, but the horns are finely articulated. In form the vessel reminds us of the bitumen or bituminous stone vessels from Susa, and also a later black terracotta vessel from Kültepe. Perhaps our vessel is related functionally to these and perhaps they all were used in cultic ceremonies. However, the ram's head is closest in style to similar heads known in publications only on large stone slabs said to have been found in Southern Russia, and also in Iranian Azerbaijan where our vessel was allegedly found. Stone bowls and pestles have also been reported from these areas and it is possible that our vessel may have been used to grind an organic material. Indeed, it may also have functioned as a portable altar.
The dating of the vessel would depend on that assigned to the stone slabs, but no firm conclusions have yet been reached. Although the slabs and our vessel have an archaic look, it is possible that they do not antedate the second or even the early first millennium B.C.

Stone; Northwestern Iranian (?); 2nd – 1st millennium B.C.
Length: 12.5 cm.; height: 6 cm.; bowl diameter: 7.8 × 8.8 cm.; depth of bowl cavity: ca. 2 cm.

BIBLIOGRAPHY: Cf. A. M. Tallgren, "Portable Altars," ESA XI (1937), 47–68; "Some North-Eurasian Sculptures," ESA XII (1938), 109–135; Karl Jettmar, "The Slab With a Ram's Head in the Rietberg Museum," Artibus Asiae XXVII, 4 (1964–5), 291–300.　　　　　(O. W. M.)

141 Ram Vessel

This vessel has the form of a recumbent ram, the body of which is hollowed out to form a bowl. Its stylized head and neck project forward boldly; its front upper legs and tail are represented in high relief, while the feet, tucked under the body, are carved almost in the round. These feet, which form the base, extend 3 cm. below the bottom of the vessel. Both horns are in high relief and partly encircle the deep socketed eyes; no mouth is depicted.

While this vessel in form is similar to the many animal-shaped vessels known from Iran, Mesopotamia and North Syria (cf. no. 135), no close parallels are known.

Grey stone; early first millennium B.C. (?)
Total height: 18.1 cm.; length: 29.1 cm.; depth of bowl: 8.5 cm.
(O.W.M.)

142 Object with Human Heads

The intended use of this object is uncertain. Open at the top and closed at the bottom, the piece could have been a vessel of some sort, except that triangular holes pierce the sides. The latter have led to the suggestion that it is an incense burner. A similar tubular object with projecting heads was excavated at Marlik in Guilan. It is open at the top and bottom and therefore certainly a mace-head. Although doubt remains as to its use, the stylistic connection between this bronze and the Marlik mace-head and the use of triangular openings, which commonly occur on bronze bells and pendants from the Caucasus, suggest a northwest Iranian provenance and a date late in the 2nd millennium B.C.

Bronze; S.W. Caspian, Iran; late 2nd millennium B.C.
Height: 10.7 cm.

BIBLIOGRAPHY: Cf. C. F. A. Schaeffer, Stratigraphie Comparée (Oxford, 1948), fig. 289 (Caucasus bronze bells and pendants with similar triangular cutouts), E. Negahban, "Notes on Some Objects from Marlik," Journal of Near Eastern Studies, vol. XXIV, 4 (1965), fig. 3. Museum of Fine Arts, Boston, Bulletin, 331, (1965), Plate 2; E. Negahban, A Preliminary Report on Marlik Excavation (Teheran, 1964), 46, no. 57, fig. 57, pl. XIII a. (P. O. H.)

143 Double-Headed Pin

Pins decorated with animal heads have a long history in the ancient Near East. In the first millennium B.C., such pins, many with addorsed animals or animal heads, are characteristic of western Iranian art. Our pin consists of two collared ram heads, placed back to back on a plinth at the head of a tapering shank, all of which is cast together. The hole at the juncture of the heads may have been to facilitate attachment to a garment, probably of wool judging from the thickness of the shank and the heaviness of the pin.

Bronze; Iranian; early first millennium B.C.
Length: 19.2 cm.

BIBLIOGRAPHY: Cf. Edward L. B. Terrace, The Art of The Ancient Near East in Boston (Boston, 1962), no. 40; Toshihko Sono, Shinji Fukai, Dailaman, III (Tokyo, 1968), pl. XLVII, 4a, b, pl. LXXX, 11 (the same pin as the Boston example); P. R. S. Moorey, Catalogue of the Persian Bronzes in the Ashmolean Museum (Oxford, 1971), 191 ff.; cf. L. Vanden Berghe, Archéologie de l'Iran ancien (Leiden, 1959), pl. 120, c; Sept Mille Ans d'Art en Iran (Paris, 1962), no. 147, pl. XIV. (O. W. M.)

144 Standard or Pole-top

Two confronted and rearing animals with rings held between their fore and hind feet are the commonest theme for such standards or pole-tops from Luristan. The pair of horses here have a fine simplicity and stylization. The bodies are typically elongated and tube-like, and the necks arched. The central elements may have been an additional piece of bronze in the form of a stylized plant. Certainly the motive of rearing animals on either side of sacred tree was a favorite one in Mesopotamia and Iran. Until scientific excavations finally produce more Luristan bronzes, however, there is no way of knowing exactly how pieces such as this were used, or at exactly what date they were made.

Bronze; Luristan, Iran; early 1st millennium B.C.
Height: 14 cm.

BIBLIOGRAPHY: 7000 ans d'art en Iran, no. 292. Cf. E. Porada, Iran Ancien (Paris, 1963), 67 ff., fig. 54.　　　　(P. O. H.)

145 Whetstone Handle with four Horse-Heads

Multiple animal heads usually occur in Luristan bronzes as projection from the shafts of axe heads, or as terminals on bracelets. The shape of this piece, as well as the bronze wire passing through the socket to assist in its attachment to the objects it held, are typical of a class of bronzes generally referred to as whetstone handles. Such handles generally end in the single head or neck of a goat, horse or lion, or, occasionally, in two heads. The four here are therefore exceptional. The horses are effectively stylized and the ears, which lie back against the neck, and the projecting forelocks give them a sense of speed and life. The flat heads are elongated triangles and there are small triangular depressions for inlay in the foreheads, another unusual feature.

Bronze; Luristan, Iran; early 1st millennium B.C.;
Length: 12 cm.

BIBLIOGRAPHY: 7000 ans d'art en Iran, no. 237. Cf. A. Godard, Ars Asiatica 17 (1931), pl. 11 (similar shape and form of attachment); Museum of Fine Arts, Boston, Bulletin, 331, (1965), Plate 3.　　　　(P. O. H.)

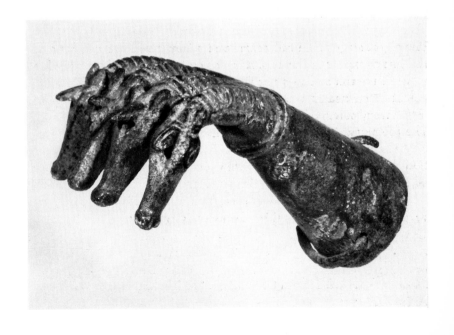

145 bis   Lion Finial

The small head is hammered from one piece of metal and all features, eyebrows, ruff, nostrils, eyes, ears, jaw, wrinkles, teeth, and tongue, were then raised; the underpart of the jaw is concave. The open mouth shows a series of ridges representing the palate, and a tongue that hangs out, overlapping the lower teeth and jaw.

Eyes without pupils are slightly raised from the front of the thick brows that project above the head. These brows consist of four ropelike swellings that abut the thick ruff below; punched dots decorate the ruff. Five raised wrinkles adorn each side of the upper jaw where they frame heavy nostrils. The neck is decorated above by parallel V-shaped ridges and below by incised lozenges. Ears are plain and heart-shaped. The overall impression is one of strong plasticity, with liberal use of linear and punched tooling.

The object stands firm but askew on its mouth without support and it does not appear to be a cup. It is also quite short and the outer edge was left uneven and was not filed smooth. Rather one may assume that it functioned as a finial, fitting snugly, without the use of nails, over a wood core, perhaps the end of a chair arm.

The prominent jaw wrinkles and the thick ruff remind us in general of the lion griffin in the Schimmel Collection (Catalogue No. 139) and also the example in the Pomerance Collection; we are also reminded of smaller cups (or finials?) in the Feroughi Collection. All these examples exhibit differences in execution and style but they may all be related in their geographical background, which seems to be Iran.

Bronze; Western Iran (?); ca. 8th—7th century B.C.
Length: 7.9 cm.; height: 7.2 cm.

BIBLIOGRAPHY: Cf. Roman Ghirshman, "Le Rhyton en Iran," Artibus Asiae XXV (1962), figures 15–17.   (O. W. M.)

146 Man with Dagger

The bearded figure wears a long straight robe belted at the waist and having a fringed hem. A dagger is stuck under the belt. On his head is a flat cap, and he wears short boots. Standing male figures in clay and bronze, with such daggers under their belts, are known from Marlik in Guilan, from Luristan and also on painted vessels from Sialk. The unusual feature of this figurine is that the arms are raised and the hands placed on either side against the head. This type of human head occurs also on iron or steel daggers from Luristan of around the 8th century B.C., leading one to propose a similar date for the Schimmel piece.

Bronze; Luristan, Iran; early 1st millennium B.C.
Height: 18 cm.

BIBLIOGRAPHY: Metropolitan Museum Exhib. Cat., no. 52; 7000 ans d'art en Iran, no. 291. Related figures in clay and bronze with daggers at their belts: 7000 ans d'art en Iran, nos. 133, 445; L. Vanden Berghe, Archéologie de l'Iran ancien (1959), pl. 124a; P. Calmeyer, Datierbare Bronzen aus Luristan und Kirmanshah (Berlin, 1969), 127 f., figs. 132, 133.

(P.O.H.)

147 Votive Statuette or Idol

Another type of Luristan bronze figurine is represented in this short-skirted human or demon. His garment is tightly belted at the waist. The head is roughly triangular in shape, and a single ropelike lock of hair ends in a curl on either side of the face. The eyes are large circles and these, with the overly prominent nose, give the figure, perhaps accidentally, a demonic appearance. The arms are bent, and the hands, in a position as if viewed from above, rest at the waist. The three-pronged base is an unusual feature, perhaps the remains of the pouring channel – left after casting.

Bronze; Luristan, Iran; early 1st millennium B.C.
Height: 13 cm.

BIBLIOGRAPHY: Queens College Exhib. Cat., no. 35; 7000 ans d'art en Iran, no. 290. (P.O.H.)

148 Stag

Small bronze stags similar to this one with magnificent branched antlers have been found in the southwest Caspian region. A Japanese expedition in that area recorded discovering such animal figurines in tombs near the waist of the body where they had originally been suspended from belts. The trunk of this stag is pierced twice horizontally. There are no details on the head itself, and the body is plain and simple, but the antlers are an elaborate and striking feature. Rather similar small bronze stags are also common in the Caucasus, where they generally have loops at the base of the neck rather than holes in the body, for suspension.

Bronze; S.W. Caspian, Iran; late 2nd millennium B.C.
Height: 9 cm.

BIBLIOGRAPHY: Cf. Illustrated London News, May 5, 1962, 699, figs. 1, 3; T. Sono, S. Fukai, Dailaman, III (Tokyo, 1968), pl. 37, 1 a–c; E. Negahban, A Preliminary Report on Marlik Excavation (Teheran, 1964), 51, no. 97, fig. 97.   (P. O. H.)

149   Vase in the Shape of a Stag

Certainly among the most striking objects found in Guilan and Mazanderan provinces on the southwest coast of the Caspian Sea, are the many pottery animal vessels. They are characteristically represented with a high degree of abstraction and are usually in the shape of bulls, rams or stags. Long before the Guilan animals appeared, a few related pieces had been discovered at Kalar Dasht in the neighboring province of Mazanderan. A pottery ram from that site has a globular body and elongated neck similar to the stag illustrated here. The extremely lightweight grayware of which this stag is made is identical to that used for some of the pottery vases excavated in 1961 near Marlik in Guilan province. Typical of the animal vessels of this culture in Guilan and Mazanderan are the large openings in the head and the use of the elongated nose as a spout. The legs are generally devoid of any articulation, and the vessels may have incised, but never painted, designs. Because other finds from Marlik show a definite connection with objects of the late 2nd millennium B.C., from the Caucasus, as well as from Sialk and Hissar in northern Iran, a date at the end of that millennium seems at this time most likely for animal vessels such as this stag.

Clay; S.W. Caspian, Iran; late 2nd millennium B.C.
Height: 16 cm.

BIBLIOGRAPHY: Cf. Illustrated London News, April 28, 1962, 663 f., and May 5, 1962, 699 ff. (Marlik excavations); L. Vanden Berghe, Archéologie de l'Iran Ancien (Leiden, 1959), pl. 3 a (pottery from Kalar Dasht). (P. O. H.)

150 Female Figure

A large group of pottery vessels and combination figurine vessels ascribed to the southwest Caspian region are made of a distinct orangeware and have round globular shapes, usually decorated with incised or punched designs. The female figurine illustrated here is of this type. The ware, as well as the style, separates this pottery from any actually excavated at Marlik, and it may be that these pieces come from a slightly different location in the same general area. The abstraction of this figurine, the masklike face, crested headdress, swelling legs and knob buttocks further differentiate this vessel from Marlik types. There are no examples, to my knowledge, of this type of figure in Luristan, but there are ties between other pottery vessels of this same orangeware and those of early 1st millennium B.C. Sialk. Future excavations will undoubtedly solve some of the problems connected with this quite striking type of pottery. At the moment, it can only be attributed in general terms to the southwest Caspian region and given a provisional date in the 1st millennium B.C.

Clay; S. W. Caspian, Iran; early 1st mill. B.C.
Height: 21.6 cm.

BIBLIOGRAPHY: Cf. E. L. B. Terrace, "Some Recent Finds From Northwest Persia", Syria, 39, 3–4 (1962), fig. 4.   (P. O. H.)

152 Ibex

The ibex stands on a rectangular bronze frame which must, in turn, have been set into some sort of a base. Between the horns there is a hole which runs vertically into the head and neck, and it is probable that the top of the piece was anchored in place by means of this hole. The position of the ibex with toes down and tail curled upward, occurs in Achaemenian times, a good example being a silver antelope in the Metropolitan Museum. The lack of surface details, however, makes a positive ascription of this piece to the Achaemenian period impossible, and it may be slightly earlier in date.

Bronze; Iran; middle of the 1st millennium B.C.
Height: 14 cm.

BIBLIOGRAPHY: Cf. Metropolitan Museum of Art Bulletin 7, no. 7 (n.s.), March 1949, 188. (P.O.H.)

151 Bitumen Roundel

This disc of bitumen is the core of a roundel originally covered with a thin layer of silver foil over which gold foil had been beaten. Fragments of the foil remain. An outer circle of crouching rams is bordered by double twisted cords. The central motif is a full-face bearded male head with twisted side-curls. A similar roundel, reputedly from the southwest Caspian region, is in the Metropolitan Museum (62.115). Assyrian reliefs represent spearmen wearing roundels attached to crossed straps at the center of the chest, presumably for protection. Such elaborate specimens as the Schimmel and Metropolitan examples would, of course, have been worn only on ceremonial occasions.

The style of the seven animals on this ornament is close to that of the finest work from Marlik, and it is likely that the piece is of the same date as the gold and silver vessels excavated there.

Bitumen with remains of silver and gold foil; Southwest Caspian; late 2nd millennium B.C.
Diameter: 9.2 cm.; thickness: 2.5 cm.

BIBLIOGRAPHY: P. Amandry, "Un motif 'Scythe' en Iran et en Grèce," JNES 24 (1965), 152, n. 21, pl. 28; P. Calmeyer in Das Tier in der Kunst Irans (Stuttgart, 1972), no. 18.

(P.O.H.)

152 bis   Relief

Extant are the upper parts of two overlapping prisoners moving right. Both hold open hands before their faces in typical suppliant fashion characteristic of Assyrian reliefs. The foreground figure is a bearded male with a knotted fillet that binds ear-length hair, and he wears a belted garment, apparently a kilt, although it is possible that sleeve lines have eroded or were accidentally omitted. The background figure is a female also wearing a fillet and a belted garment. She has a round, heavy chin, and her lips and nose are thicker and rounder than the male's; also, the distance from her lips to her chin is shorter than that from the male's lips to his beard. Under a raking light, vertical hair lines are visible above and below both figures' fillets.

On the basis of the knotted fillet it would seem that these figures are Elamites, and it is possible that they formed part of the reliefs depicting their defeat by Ashurbanipal in 653 B.C.

The fragment is now only 6 mm. in width – not measuring the relief proper – having been cut down to a smoothe surface to facilitate transportation. Neither the rear surface nor the edges exhibit evidence of recent cutting; the surface is badly weathered.

Grey stone; Assyrian; probably from the period of Ashurbanipal, after 653 B.C.

Extant height: 27.2 cm.; extant width: 17 cm.

BIBLIOGRAPHY: Cf. R. D. Barnett, Assyrian Palace Reliefs (London, 1960), figs. 117 ff.   (O. W. M.)

153   Winged-Bull Cauldron Attachment

Winged-bull attachments placed on cauldrons were popular in Greece and the Near East in the eighth and seventh centuries B.C. This example probably was made in Iran and is the mate to the attachment now in The Metropolitan Museum.

The attachment consists of the head, neck, and chest of a bull cast solid together with the wings and tail of a bird. Attached to the tail is a free-swinging ring serving as a handle. The bull's horns and ears project forward; its nostrils are formed by two shallow depressions; facial details are created with shallow grooves. There is a rounded forelock decorated in zones with hatching marks; touching the forelock on either side are two oval eyes and thick eyebrows plastically rendered. Wings and tail are decorated with a plain feather pattern. Stylized hair markings exist at the back of the head and hair tassles are on the sides of the neck.

Bronze; Iranian; ca. 7th–6th centuries B.C.
Wing span: 15.6 cm.; length from tail to horns: 14.1 cm.

BIBLIOGRAPHY: Oscar White Muscarella, "Winged Bull Cauldron Attachments from Iran," Metropolitan Museum of Art Journal I (1968), 7–18; Peter Calmeyer, Datierbare Bronzen aus Luristan und Kirmanshah (Berlin, 1969), 109–110.   (O. W.M.)

154 Relief Mirror

The mirror, of cast and chased bronze, is decorated with a pair of lions contained within a circle of thirty three rosettes, each rosette having twelve petals. The lions stand on their hind legs, back to back, with their heads turned so that they face each other, nose touching nose. A front paw of one lion is pressed against that of the other. The two tails are intertwined. All semblance of realism has been discarded in favor of a symmetrical and interesting pattern. The pose suggests that of pairs of lions in some Achaemenid gold roundels, of which examples are in the Metropolitan Museum of Art and in the Oriental Institute, Chicago, though these are more naturalistic. The manner in which the musculature of the shoulders is treated in the animals on the bronze mirror is thoroughly Achaemenid in style. The mirror originally had a handle which has now disappeared. It was attached by means of seven iron pins which were arranged in such a fashion that five of them formed a small semicircle, with the other two on the central axis. Some of the pins still remain, much corroded with black and red oxide. It will be noticed that if the mirror were to be held up by a vertical handle the lions would be upside down, which leads one to conjecture that the handle may have had a loop or some means of suspension so that they would be the right way up when the mirror was not in use.

Bronze; Achaemenid; 5th century B.C.
Height (max.): 22.8 cm.; diameter: 21.7 cm.

BIBLIOGRAPHY: Cf. Helene J. Kantor, "Achaemenid Jewelry in the Oriental Institute", JNES 16 (1957), 16, pl. 9. Museum of Fine Arts, Boston, Bulletin, 331 (1965), Plate 18; Trésors de l'ancien Iran, Musée Rath, Geneva (1966), Cat. No. 660; R. W. Hamilton, "A Silver Bowl in the Ashmolean Museum," Iraq 28 (1966), 8 ff.; Andrew Oliver, "A Bronze Mirror from Sardis," Studies Presented to George M. A. Hanfmann, ed., David Gordon Mitten (Mainz, 1971), 119, n. 32. Oliver claims that the relief was added to the original mirror at a later time; however, the mirror was recently examined in the research laboratory of the Römisch-Germanisches Zentralmuseum, Mainz. In a report dated February 6, 1973 Professor H. J. Hundt and Messrs. Folz and Lehóczky, who examined the surface of the relief under high magnification, reject the possibility of a re-working: "Die Metallstrukturen schliessen eine sekundäre Meisselarbeit mit Sicherheit aus. Das Löwenrelief ist gegossen, die Konturen sind mit dem Meissel nachgearbeitet ... Am linken Hinterschenkel des linken Löwen (und an mehreren anderen Stellen) ist die glänzende Patina durchgehend auch in den ziselierten Linien erhalten". (C. K. W.)

155 Rhyton

The rhyton was acquired in many pieces and has been restored without difficulty to its original shape. The whole protome, which is in the form of the upper body and head of a ram, and most of the cup, except for sections of the repoussé ram's body, are complete. The rhyton was originally constructed of eleven pieces of silver: one for the cup and ten for the protome. The protome unit consists of two identical pieces, each representing one half of the body, neatly joined together at the center, giving the effect of one unit hammered from a single piece. All the body and head features – shoulders, legs, muzzle, lips, curls, eyes, eyebrows, and forelock – were raised from behind. Details of these features – forelock and curl markings, eye pupils, and leg markings – were incised with masterful precision and skill. Horns and ears were added by solder.

The top of the ram's head is almost horizontal before it sharply curves down to the back; its neck is thick and is almost at right angles to the head. The horns sweep back gracefully and are completely decorated with incised wavy lines representing the bony structure. Small ears are set vertically between the horns and develop from two lobes executed in repoussé. A row of spiral curls, outlined on one side by two incised lines, joins the lobes to the lip. The same type of curl can be seen on the chest and on the back of the neck.

Eyes are round with an incised pupil, and there is a tear duct. Eyebrows consist of three concentric plain loops framing the eye at top and outer side. A curved forelock, consisting of five loops, each decorated by incised lines, is framed by the eyebrows.

A slight depression exists on either side of the muzzle, and a swelling depicts the lips. Two grooves on the front of the muzzle complete the decoration. The legs are folded back under the body, and the knees project almost to the face line. A tulip design, in repoussé, adorns each leg, and veins and hooves are incised. Shoulders are represented by an oval bulge outlined by grooves. There is a hole in the chest just above the knee line into which a tube was presumably added to facilitate pouring. The truncated cup section narrows from top to bottom where it curves gently to join the protome section. The body, tail, and rear legs of the ram are represented in repoussé along the walls of the cup, thus continuing and completing the forepart from the protome. The body is plain except for neatly incised "wings" on each side, two incised body creases on the left side, and a row of spiral curls like those on the head (but here incised) running from the tail along the back. Leg and hoof lines are also incised. Neat, uniform fluting begins below the neck and extends, except where the body is represented, to the join area. The lip curves out and is dipped on the outside for pouring. A pattern of alternating linked palmettos and lotuses, below which is a narrow guilloche band, decorates the neck. This floral motif includes linking stems that are incised with double lines; a semi-oval design is pendent from the base of each lotus and palmetto.

A small strainer was reportedly found with the rhyton fragments. It is an oval silver disc with ten holes arranged in a triangle, punched from one side, and a larger hole above punched from the other; its diameter is 3.2 by 3.7 cm. A thin silver sheet, partly preserved, was soldered to the rear edges of the disc in order to hold the strainer in place at the join between cup and protome. A now-missing ring must have masked the join on the outside (as in the Seven Brothers' rhyton).

The Schimmel rhyton fits easily into the repertory of known Achaemenian examples. Horizontally fluted cups are common, and some examples also have their necks decorated with floral patterns and a guilloche. And at least one rhyton, of terracotta, probably of late Achaemenian date (and surprisingly also in the Schimmel collection, cat. no. 162), has the animal's body, a winged lion, represented in relief against the walls of the cup. Two rhyta, however, stand out as being closest in style and technique of manufacture to this one: the horn rhyton terminating in an ibex head from the Seven Brothers group of kurgans, and one in the form of the complete body of a ram, which is in a private collection in Paris (unpublished). The most striking similarity is the use of two pieces of silver, each representing half of the head, in the construction of the heads. In addition, all three share the thick neck, eye, eyebrow and mouth details, the forelock with decorated loops, the spiral curls on the ruff, and the leg position.

The Paris rhyton has spiral-curl decoration on the neck and chest, although at an angle, upright ears, body "wing" design, and the same type of horns with wavy decoration. The Seven Brothers' rhyton also has double ear lobes, and, although its ears are now missing, they probably were upright.

Besides these rhyta, there is a straight-cup rhyton terminating in a ram's head, found in the eighteenth century in Russia, and now in Leningrad, that also has the same basic horn type and decoration, the same type of forelock and eyebrows, and a very similar guilloche and floral pattern on its neck.

Differences in detail and in general shape do exist among the rhyta, to be sure, but the similarities are extensive enough to suggest that they may have been made by the same workshop. At the same time it is necessary to point out that Achaemenian art is not always easy to date precisely, for it seems that particular canonical concepts and details continued to be used over a long period of time. Thus one cannot be certain that the same artists were involved in the construction of all these rhyta, or that they were all necessarily made within a few years of one another.

An indication for a general date for these rhyta is the fact that the one from the Seven Brothers group was found with material dated to the first half of the fifth century B.C. Thus it is probable that they were made roughly between 500 and 450 B.C.

Silver; Achaemenian; ca. first half of the fifth century B.C.
Cup height: ca. 20 cm.; lip diameter: 12 by 12.3 cm., height of ram without horns: ca. 10 cm.

Bibliography: Cf. B. Svoboda, "Zur Geschichte des Rhytons," in Neue Denkmäler Antiker Toreutik (Prague, 1956), passim, and pp. 36 ff., 46 ff., 55 ff.; Herbert Hoffmann, "The Persian Origin of the Greek Rhyton," Antike Kunst 4 (1961), 21–29; Klaus Tuchelt, Tiergefässe in Kopf- und Protomengestalt (Berlin, 1962), 59 ff. See also the recently published bent terracotta rhyton from Leilan, near Mianduab in Northwest Iran: W. Kleiss, "Bericht über Erkundungsfahrten in Iran im Jahre 1971," AMI 5 (1972), 157 f., fig. 30, pl. 39. This rhyton is probably close to ca. 600 B.C. in date and appears to be Iranian, not Urartian.   (O. W. M.)

156   Cloisonné Earring

The earring is in the form of a circle broken by an opening containing a hinged catch for attachment to the ear. On both sides of an interior area that consists of a gold sheet are decorated disc cloisons. Above cloisonné double wings in the prominent central disc, the upper part of Ahura Mazda, in profile, holding a flower is depicted; an outer border of triangular cloisons encloses the scene. Three cloisons, showing the same figure smaller and rising from a half-moon flank the central disc; a seventh cloison containing a lotus is placed at the lower center. While all the small cloissons are connected directly to the central one, they are separated from each other by a lozenge incised with a small circle.

Framing the discs is a border of triangles, like that enclosing the central disc, and an openwork floral pattern, the outer part of which contains inlays. The Ahura Mazda figures and the lozenges were cut from pieces of gold and have incised features, while the cloisons contained inlays, of which only turquoise now remains.

The mate for this earring is now in the Boston Museum of Fine Arts; besides turquoise, carnelian and lapis lazuli inlays are preserved. Earrings similar in form or decoration have been excavated in Iran in a tomb at Susa and in a hoard from Pasargadae. Also, a motiv similar to that of the Ahura Mazda figure above the half-moon exists on a button and on a necklace element found in the Susa tomb just mentioned. These examples are dated from the late fifth to the mid-fourth century B.C., and our earring surely fits within this time period.

Gold; Achaemenian; late fifth- mid-fourth century B.C.
Diameter: 6 cm.; thickness: 3 mm.

BIBLIOGRAPHY: Cf. William Kelly Simpson, "Acquisitions in Egyptian and Ancient Near Eastern Art...," The Connoisseur (Feb., 1972), fig. 8; D. Stronach, "Excavations at Pasargadae: Third Preliminary Report," Iran III (1965), 33, 38 f., pl. XI a–c; J. de Morgan, Délégation en Perse Memoirés VIII (1905), 50 ff., figs. 78–80, pl. V.   (O. W. M.)

156 bis   Scabbard Chape

A very distinctive scabbard (akinakes) is portrayed on reliefs at Persepolis and Naqsh-i-Rustam, carried by Medes, Scythians, six eastern tribes, and the Thracians, the Armenians, and the Cappadocians. It is characterized by a curved, stylized projection from one side of the top that held a thong for suspension from the belt, and a separately made trefoil tip or chape. Examples of this scabbard type, made of gold, are known from Russian excavations and from the Oxus Treasure, which also contained a gold plaque depicting a man wearing the same scabbard. Trefoil chapes of bronze, ivory, and gold, displaced from their scabbards, also exist.

Some of the chapes on the Persepolis reliefs are plain while others are decorated with a highly stylized animal, both lion- and dog-like, which curves back so that its head touches its hindquarters. Only the head is rendered naturalistically, while the heart-shaped ear, filled with a floral motif, concentric thick flesh folds, and the lack of recognizable limbs, demonstrate a keen sense of abbreviation and stylization. The displaced chapes have the same features, although some depict rams, or a ram's head above a lion. Portrayal of animals in this manner clearly derives from earlier Scythian and apparently Median sources.

The displaced chape here is cast, with two holes on top of the flat back. The animal is closely paralleled both by those on the Persepolis reliefs (in the Treasury, Council Hall) and by others for example an ivory one with a ram's body in the Louvre.

Bronze; Achaemenian, sixth-fifth century B.C.
Height: 6.7 cm.; width: 6.7 cm.

BIBLIOGRAPHY: Cf. Ernst Herzfeld, Iran in the Ancient East (Oxford, 1941), 265 f., figs. 367, 368, pl. 84, lower right; Bernard Goldman, "Achaemenian Chapes," Ars Orientalis II (1957), 43–54; Roman Ghirshman, The Arts of Ancient Iran (New York, 1964), figs. 109, 118, 287, 288, 365; Edith Porada, The Art of Ancient Iran (New York, 1965), 140, fig. 76.   (O. W. M.)

157   Horse Ornament

These small objects, usually in the form of a griffin's or ram's head, and with the short shaft doubly pierced at right angles, were used to hold several bridle straps on a horse's reins. Examples in bone and metal are known from Russia, Iran, Iraq, Urartu, and Asia Minor, dating from the seventh century B.C. and later. Their origin is attributed to the Scythians. Plain curved examples in bronze have been found at Persepolis and are represented on reliefs there, thus documenting their use in the Achaemenid period. Our example is in the form of a horse's head with a narrow clipped mane, a knob on the top of the head, and pouches at the cheek.

Similar types of horses' heads are known from representations of the Achaemenid period, and it would seem that this ornament dates to that time.

Silver; Achaemenian, fifth-fourth century B.C.
Height: 2.8 cm.

BIBLIOGRAPHY: Cf. Ernst E. Herzfeld, Iran in the Ancient East (Oxford, 1941), 271, fig. 374, pls. 77, 79; Erich Schmidt, Persepolis I (Chicago, 1953), pls. 35, 37, 42, 52; Persepolis II (Chicago, 1957), pl. 79; H. H. von der Osten, Die Welt der Perser (Stuttgart, 1956), pl. 63, below; B. B. Piotrovskii, Vanskoie Tsarstvo (Moscow, 1959), 242, fig. 82; Tamara T. Rice, The Scythians (London, 1958), 191, fig. 48.   (O. W. M.)

This elaborately decorated handle of cast silver with chased details may originally have terminated in a spoon. The animals heads are those of a duck, a lion and a calf, and they are executed with exquisite delicacy and great exactness of detail. The final head cannot be that of a swan, as has been claimed, since it has ears and teeth. This must be some fantastic animal. Although the motive of an animal head spitting out the head and neck of another creature is fairly common in Iran, where it was often employed for bracelets, it had no popularity before the Achaemenid period.

Lion heads spitting out blades of dagger or axes are common enough on Luristan bronzes, but animals emerging from the mouths of other animals are never represented. A somewhat similar idea can be found in Urartu (Van), where a tall lamp-stand, now in Hamburg, has legs in the form of lions from whose mouth the leg and foot of a bull emerge. It may be that this type of decoration originated in Urartu or in Syria and passed thence into both Achaemenid and northern Nomad art.

Silver; Achaemenid; ca. 5th century B.C.
Length: 9.4 cm.

BIBLIOGRAPHY: P. Amandry, "Orfèvrerie achéménide," Antike Kunst 1 (1958), 13, pl. 10, nos. 15–16; Metropolitan Museum Exhib. Cat., no. 41; D. Stronach, "Excavations at Pasargadae, Third Preliminary Report," Iran III (1965), pl. XII, a, b; Ruth Amiran, "Achaemenian Bronze Objects from a Tomb at Kh. Ibsan...," Levant IV (1972), 136 f., pl. XIII, left, and fig. 3. Cf. Hoffmann-Hewicker, Kunst des Altertums im Museum für Kunst und Gewerbe, Hamburg (1961), figs. 16–17 (Hamburg lampstand).
Iranische Kunst im Deutschen Museum, Landesmuseum Karlsruhe, Antiken Abt. Nr. 3 A Armreifen, Franz Steiner Verlag (Wiesbaden).
(C. K. W.)

159 Ibex Handle

The use of zoomorphic handles on amphora-shaped vessels achieved great popularity during the Achaemenid period in Iran. In bronze, silver, silver gilt or gold, the handles represent ibexes, horses and bulls, winged at times, and fantastic conglomerate monsters. The bent knees of this ibex originally rested on the rim of a vessel and the hind legs, when complete, would have joined the sides somewhere at, or just below, the shoulder. A silver vessel with a pair of handles quite similar to this one is in the Archaeological Museum in Teheran.

Silver; Achaemenid; ca. 5th century B.C.; length: 7.5 cm.

BIBLIOGRAPHY: P. Amandry, "Toreutique Achéménide," Antike Kunst 2 (1959), 38 ff. Cf. 7000 ans d'art en Iran, no. 684, pl. 55 (similar piece in Teheran Museum).   (C. K. W.)

160 Lion Head Finial

This small finial is made of two pieces of gold, one for the head and neck of the lion, the other for the tongue, which slightly protrudes, and for the roof of the mouth. Details of the face are in repoussé, and the design of the mane is chased. Inside the mouth, even the ridges of the roof have been indicated in repoussé, in spite of the fact that they are only visible on very close observation. Small triangles of granulation and twisted wire are soldered on around the rim. Such care and attention to detail is typical of the best Achaemenian work.

Two holes pierce the edge where gold-headed nails would have secured the lion-head to the piece of royal furniture or equipment it originally adorned.

Gold; Achaemenid; ca. 5th century B.C.
Length: 8.2 cm.; diameter: 5 cm.

BIBLIOGRAPHY: Metropolitan Museum Exhib. Cat., no. 42; Jewish Museum Exhib. Cat., no. 112; 7000 ans d'art en Iran, no. 689, pl. 67, bottom right.   (C. K. W.)

The main decoration is composed of four ibexes walking in a counter-clockwise direction. They are complete but for one which has lost part of its horn. The ibexes, an outer rim and a circular band, which is touched by the tips of the horns, are higher than the surrounding surface, which has been carved away leaving a very thin background that was lacking in several places and has been restored. In the center, within the circular band, a gold repoussé rosette, with a sepal between the sixteen petals, is attached by means of silver pins which pierce it between pairs of circular projections. Each projection is approximately 1.5 to 2 mm. in diameter. There are sixteen pins and thirty two projections.

The ibexes at first sight appear to be typically Achaemenid, but a closer examination reveals certain differences from any known work of art of the Achaemenid period. These are to be noted particularly in the conventional treatment of the rib cage and the "corded" outline of the rump which begins – or ends – with a curl in the middle of the back. The ribs are indicated in a form that resembles a curved half-leaf that is attached by a curling stem to the muscles of the shoulder. Although these details are unknown in Achaemenid art they occur on a gold gorget (mistakenly called a pectoral) from the Ziwiyeh treasure now in the Archaeological Museum in Teheran. The gorget is decorated with various mythological monsters and also with two naturalistic ibexes standing on their hind legs. The latter have these same peculiarities as the ibexes on our silver bowl. The date of the gorget would seem to be seventh century B.C. Cyrus did not come into power before 550 B.C. The relationship between the two works of art is unmistakable. If they are indeed contemporary, the bowl would show the beginnings of the Achaemenid style – though the actual details were later to be somewhat changed. If the bowl is of the Achaemenid period, it shows how closely details of an earlier art persisted into the sixth century.

Silver and gold; early Achaemenid; 6th century B.C.
Diameter: 29.9 cm.

BIBLIOGRAPHY: Cf. A. Godard, Le Trésor de Ziwiyé (Haarlem, 1950), figs. 10, 13; Museum of Fine Arts, Boston, Bulletin, 331, 1965, Plate 11; Trésors de l'Ancien Iran, Geneva, Musée Rath (1966), Plate 48, Cat. No. 628. Cf. The Pomerance Collection of Ancient Art (Brooklyn, 1966), 50 f., no. 58; cf. P. Jacobsthal, Greek Pins (Oxford, 1956), 179, nos. 591, 592.   (C. K. W.)

162 Rhyton: Winged Horned Lion

Clay like no. 163. Missing horns, forelegs and the tip of the right ear. Red color (mouth, nostrils, horns, ears).

A winged lion with ibex horns (missing) that sweep back to engage the beaker is represented in a gracefully arching leap. His mouth is open and tongue pendant. Only the protome of the animal is represented in the round; trunk, hind legs and wings are indicated in relief against the walls of the fluted beaker (cf. cat. no. 155). A short spout protrudes from the chest, much as in the horse-rhyton, no. 163. Unlike the latter however, there is little that can be considered Hellenic in the style of this example. Its forms are Achaemenid Persian, harking back to the late period of Persepolis. A similar instance of archaizing Persianism in the art of the Hellenistic east is afforded by the stone lion-monsters from Belevi, in the courtyard of the Ephesus Museum. Handleless rhyta such as this example were placed in stands when not in use. (See no. 155.)

Terracotta; from near Adana Cappadocian; 4th–3rd centuries B.C.
Height: 29.7 cm.   (H. H.)

163　Rhyton: Galloping Horse

Coarse and highly micaceous grey clay; burnished. Left leg and fragment of rim restored. The great trumpet-like bowl of the rhyton terminates in the protome of a galloping horse. The reins are rendered three-dimensionally and in relief, and the details of the bridle are added in red color. Discs of clay are applied to simulate metal embellishments. The top of the mane is tied into a foreknot. A short spout occupies the area between the horse's legs. The manner of drinking from such rhyta is illustrated on a late Attic bell-krater in Vienna (H. Hoffmann, Antike Kunst 4 [1961], pl. 12,1): the banqueter held the rhyton aloft, allowing a jet of wine to spurt into a phiale held in the other hand. The purpose of this action was the aeration of the wine, which apparently improved the flavour. The custom is of Iranian origin, and this type of drinking vessel is derived from Persian prototypes.

The Schimmel rhyton is related to fourth-century Greek rhyta in precious metal, such as the famous example from Duvanlij and the less well-known one in Prague (Svoboda-Conçev, Neue Denkmäler antiker Toreutik (Prague, 1956), pls. 8 and 1–4, resp.). Related rhyta in terracotta include an example from Cappadocia (Svoboda-Conçev, note 172, pl. 7 a–b), perhaps a product of the same workshop as our example. The annular joint between the beaker and the horse-protome appears to be a rudimentary survival in clay of a functional detail of the metal prototype.

Terracotta; from near Adana; Cappadocian; Probably 3rd century B.C.
Height: 35 cm.　　　　　　　　　　　　　　　　　(H. H.)

164 Animal Handle

Cast in the form of a springing panther or leopard with open mouth, this animal has large round ears, oval eyes that apparently once held an inlay, and a tail that extends straight out between his outstretched rear legs and curls up at the tip. While the interior of the body from rear to front legs is hollow, the head and neck are solid.

Handles such as these were used in the Parthian and Sasanian periods to hold vessels and incense burners.

Bronze; Parthian; ca. 2nd century B.C. – 2nd century A.D.
Length: 10.8 cm.

BIBLIOGRAPHY: Cf. Roman Ghirshman, Iran Parthians and Sassanians (London 1964), 273, fig. 356; Louis Vanden Berghe, Archéologie de l'Iran Ancien (Leiden, 1959), pl. 124, b; Kunstschätze aus Iran (Zurich, 1962), pl. 58, no. 882.   (O. W. M.)

165   Gazelle Head

The animal depicted is probably a gazelle. Attached to the long curved and ribbed horns are wires terminating in paste and carnelian beads and a gold disc decorated with punched dots on the outer border. The eyes are inlaid with carnelian beads; the mouth is a thin slit. Both the eyes and the base of the horns are encircled by granulation. The back of the head is plain and flat but there is a small hole on each side of the neck. It is not clear how this object was used but perhaps it was applied to a diadem.

The head and a mate, now in a collection in Switzerland, is said to have come from the southwest Caspian area. Parallels do not seem to be available but the object could be Parthian.

Gold; southwest Caspian (?); Parthian (?), ca. 2nd century.B.C. – 2nd century A.D.
Height: 7.5 cm.   (O. W. M.)

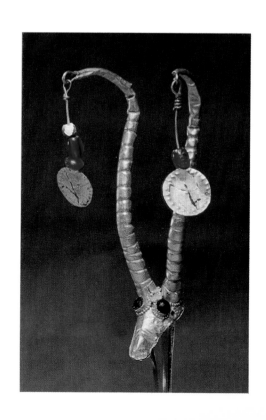

166   Belt Plaque

This rectangular plaque was cast together with bosses at each corner and borders decorated by bands of cast herringbone design. Its interior open-work decoration consists of highly stylized animals, not easily identifiable but apparently a stag and animals of prey; the animals are hollow at the rear. Also at the rear are a hook at one edge and a ring at the other.

These plaques are reportedly from the Caucasus, particularly from Georgia. Recent research suggests that they probably were made late in the first millennium B.C.

Bronze; Caucasian; late first millennium B.C.
Height: 12.3 cm.; width: 12.8 cm.

BIBLIOGRAPHY: First published by Ann Farkas in 'Animal Style' Art from East to West (Asia Society, 1970), 47, 57, fig. 37; see also Kunstschätze aus Iran (Kunsthaus Zürich, 1962), 185, no. 888, fig. 34.
(O. W. M.)

167 Oval Bowl

Grape clusters and leaves frame a running tigress on both sides of this cast silver bowl. Its low, hollow, grooved base was added separately. The stripes on the tigress and grapes are inlaid with niello. An inscription in typical dotted lettering occurs within the base and reads, according to Christopher J. Brunner: 's-iiiiii, asēmēn šaš," "of silver, 6 (drahms)," which, typically, is only a fraction of the bowl's actual weight. There is also an artisan's device at the right. The shape of the bowl and the style of the inscription suggest a date late in the Sasanian period. One half of the bowl has been cleaned.

Silver; Sasanian period, ca. 6th–7th century A.D.
Length: 16.3 cm.; width: 9.8 cm.

BIBLIOGRAPHY: Oleg Grabar, Sasanian Silver (University of Michigan Museum of Art, 1967), 41 f., 115, no. 28; Prudence Oliver Harper in "Origins and Influence," BMMA (March 1971), 324 f.   (O. W. M.)

168 Rhyton

Blown glass with twisted rope handles applied. Although this vessel appears to be an amphora, the small flat base is pierced by a hole so that it is, in fact, a rhyton. Wheel-cut facets decorate the body. The delicacy of the shape and the subtle variation in the size of the hexagonal facets are indications of the extremely high quality of the piece.

The shape, as well as the faceted decoration, link this vessel closely to glass of the Roman empire. During the Parthian and Sasanian periods, Roman craftsmen were active in Iran, and the technique of glassmaking common in the Roman empire could easily have been brought by them to the Near East.

Before the recent discoveries in the southwest Caspian region, little glass from the Parthian and Sasanian periods had been found in Iran. Now it appears that much glassware of extremely high quality existed in both periods. Whether it came by the trade routes from the eastern Mediterranean, or whether it was made somewhere in the area in which so much of it has been found, cannot as yet be answered. It is remarkable that this delicate and graceful piece is still intact, and this suggests that it was found in a tomb.

Glass; S. W. Caspian, Iran; ca. 3rd century A.D.
Height: 32 cm.

For glass vessels recently excavated in the S. W. Caspian, see F. Shinji, "A Persian Treasure in the Shosoin Repository", Japan Quarterly, April–June 1960; cf. also A. von Saldern, Ars Orientalis 5 (1963), 7 ff.　　　　　　　　　(P. O. H.)

EGYPT

Probably all the terms for materials used in this section will be familiar to anyone conversant with the literature of art history with the probable exception of 'Egyptian blue'. This very unsatisfactory term describes not a color but a material earlier known as 'frit' and even today frequently (not incorrectly) described as 'glass paste' and 'pate de verre'. It is an opaque substance, always blue or blue-green with matte surface and in composition and appearance about half way between glass and faience. It was in use throughout Egyptian history and is found in many other cultures as well. It occurs frequently in classical studies under the name *kyanos*. It was always molded and fired and shows enormous variation in composition and texture during the long period of its manufacture.

Chemically, it consists of a fine sand, copper carbonate, calcium carbonate and sodium carbonate.

169 Tomb Relief

From the chapel of an official whose name is lost. The column with the usual offering formula refers to "the priestess of Hathor, Irty" who was presumably the official's wife. The flesh is red, the necklace and hieroglyphs are blue. The block comes from the lower right corner of the recess in which a false door was located.

Limestone; Late VI Dynasty (ca. 2350–2280 B.C.)
Height: 63 cm.

BIBLIOGRAPHY: Metropolitan Museum Exhib. Cat., no. 63. A companion piece is in the von Kienbusch collection in Princeton University, N. J. Time Magazine Dec. 13, 1959, page 33.

(J. D. C.)

170 Companion of the Dead

The statuette in ivory shows a standing woman, her arms at her sides. Her wig terminates in four long braids, which are undercut. Her very narrow waist is encircled by a belt, and her hips are wide. The feet, probably made separately, are missing. The sculpture closely follows limestone figures of comparable use and date and was clearly made as a concubine figure. Scattered patches of the original surface are preserved. They show that the sculpture was highly polished, as were so many other ivory statuettes of this period. It is unlikely that any paint was used.

Ivory; XII Dynasty (ca. 2000–1780 B.C.).
Height: 10.4 cm.

From the Omar Pasha Sultan Collection.   (J. D. C.)

171 Companion of the Dead

Statuette of a concubine now incomplete but probably extending only to the knees. A braided wig covers the front half of the head, the back of which is partly shaved with the hair arranged in braids. The wig, hair and decorations on the body are painted black.

Limestone; XII Dynasty (ca. 2000–1780 B.C.)
Height: 8.2 cm.   (J. D. C.)

172   Seal

A cynocephalus ape in white steatite glazed blue, matte finish, sits with his hands resting on his knees. The base which has a curved front is decorated with an incised pattern of a loop or cord. As this animal was a sacred animal the object was probably an amulet as well as a seal.

XII Dynasty (ca. 2000–1780 B.C.).
Height: 3.2 cm.   (J. D. C.)

173   Genre Group

At one end a young boy, nude and with side-lock, squats on the ground coaxing the spotted dog which stands stiffly at the opposite end. The boy's side-lock, his finger and foot nails, the dog's spots and sides of the base are glazed very dark blue, all other areas being lighter blue. This informal composition must have been made as a toy or simply as decoration, and it is difficult to understand why it should have been placed in a tomb. A close duplicate from Lisht is in the Metropolitan Museum of Art.

Fayence; XII Dynasty (ca. 2000–1780 B.C.).
Height: 4.1 cm.; length: 9.5 cm.   (J. D. C.)

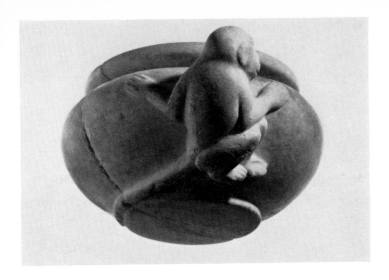

174 Marble Bowl

A bowl in gray-blue marble with a monkey almost entirely in the round climbing up towards the rim. His long tail curls around the foot of the bowl. A very fine example of work in this medium. A fragment of a similar bowl is in the Kestner Museum in Hanover. The bowl, the preceding three objects and a small unpublished fayence hippopotamus are said to have been found together.

Anhydrite; XII Dynasty (ca. 2000–1780 B.C.).
Height: 3.5 cm.; diameter: 7.6 cm.

BIBLIOGRAPHY: Kayser, fig. 36; E. L. B. Terrace, Journal of the American Research Center in Egypt, v. V, (Cambridge, 1966), p. 59 (1) and pl. XIV.   (J. D. C.)

175 Toilet Implement

This ivory rod, circular in section, terminates in an ibex head, while its undecorated end is rounded; there are no remains of paint. The object is complete in its present condition, but its use is unknown. Duplicate examples fitted with a spoon are known.

Ivory; Middle Kingdom.
Length: 13.8 cm.

BIBLIOGRAPHY: Ingrid Wallert, Der verzierte Löffel, seine Formgeschichte und Verwendung im alten Ägypten (Wiesbaden, 1967), p. 86, pl. 7 (C6).
(J. D. C.)

176 Monkey in Amethyst

A seated monkey clasps her baby directly in front of her. The head of the young one is now lost. The mother leans slightly forward, creating a feeling of great tenderness. A suspension hole has been drilled from each side at the back just below the shoulder level. This little sculpture in amethyst of the finest deep purple color is certainly without religious significance. The subject and composition were already known in the late Old Kingdom.

Amethyst; XII Dynasty (ca. 2000–1780 B.C.).
Height: 3.6 cm.   (J. D. C.)

177 Ointment Vessel

This vase in translucent amethystine quartz is of a traditional shape that had its origin in the Old Kingdom. The base is circular, and the cylindrical lower body flares to a relatively thick, overhanging rim. Doubtless there was originally a disk cover. Patches of deep and brilliant amethyst are scattered over the body alternating with areas of yellowish and colorless stone. This is a simple object of great beauty.

Stone; probably XII Dynasty (ca. 2000–1780 B.C.).

Formerly in the collection of the Textile Museum, Washington, D.C.   (J. D. C.)

178 Figure from a Boat

It is not at all surprising that this squatting figure of an owner is wrapped in a white cloak, but it is very unusual to find that he is made of stone, since wood is the much more common medium. He wears a close-fitting wig, his skin is painted red, and his eyes are black. The base has been drilled for inserting the sculpture onto a peg. Because the stone was crumbling, the entire surface has been saturated with cellulose acetate in acetone.

Limestone; Middle Kingdom.
Height: 5 cm. (J. D. C.)

179 Head from a Statuette

The small male head in compact dark green stone has an ovoid skull with large flaring ears and conventionalized features. His thick lips display a slightly smiling expression. The greater part of the back of the head is lost. This is a good example of a standard type of the later Middle Kingdom.

Stone; probably late XII Dynasty.
Height: 4.1 cm. (J. D. C.)

180 Sleepy Hippopotamus

About to doze off, this recumbent hippopotamus is of blue-green faience, glazed on all surfaces. Four large lotus blossoms, painted in manganese, are symmetrically arranged around the body, one at each end, the others centered on each side. Two rosettes or conventionalized flowers formed of a circle centered within dots are arranged on each side of the body. The eyes and snout are also in manganese. On each side of the jaw are two unidentified, curious u-like forms.

Faience; XII Dynasty.
Length: 8.2 cm. (J. D. C.)

181 Statuette of a Lady

The lady depicted in this standing statuette wears the usual close-fitting, low-cut dress of the period. She also wears bracelets and anklets. Her large wig, parted in the center and falling down in back and in front, is now black but may originally have been blue. Her eyes are outlined in metal, presumably copper, and inlaid with opaque white stone and obsidian (?).

The long arms were carved separately and the fingernails painted white. The legs along with the tiny base on which the lady stands may have been carved separately as well, but this is uncertain. In any case, the completed composition was inserted into an oblong base of much softer wood – apparently an economy move. This base was given a white undercoat over which red paint was applied. A two-line inscription, which is now in part defaced, was rapidly written across the front of the base in black ink. It commences somewhat abruptly with an abbreviated version of the traditional offering formula, "An invocation of bread and beer, oxen and fowl, for the ka of ... hetep, justified."

It is tempting to consider this lady as the wife of Seneb. Certainly the inscriptions on the two sculptures are by the same hand, but this fact may indicate nothing more than an origin in the same shop. Probably both sculptures are from Chassinat's excavations at Deir el-Durunka.

Ebony; early XII Dynasty (ca. 2000–1780 B.C.).
Height without base: 24.7 cm., with base: 27.5 cm.

BIBLIOGRAPHY: Sultan, no. 223, pl. XXXIX.　　　　　(J. D. C.)

182　Statuette of Seneb

Depicted in soft wood, perhaps sycamore, this man stands frontally with his arms at his sides and his left leg advanced. He has a shaved, ovoid head with relatively low, slightly flaring ears. Painted areas are the black eyes and eyebrows, white fingernails, long white skirt, and the red base. The torso and arms are apparently stained. The sculpture was made in nine separate parts: the head and torso as a single unit, the arms, the lower body with skirt, the legs, the front parts of the feet, and the base. This piece is held in place by a long wooden pin inserted on the left side of the base and passing through dowels on the undersides of the feet. Across the front of the base is a two-line black inscription showing a strong influence of hieratic. It is now considerably faded, but it seems to say "The revered one, the Osiris, the (scribe) of royal records, Seneb, justified." Except for the title, this reading is reasonably certain. Literally, that section reads "royal document," which is without meaning in this context. It is apparently an abbreviation for some office connected with royal records along the lines I have suggested. This sculpture is probably a companion to a piece long in the collection of the Walters Art Gallery in Baltimore. As the Baltimore statuette exactly parallels this sculpture, even to its being made in nine parts, there is no necessity to describe it. It too had an inscription on the base, now almost entirely defaced. Both sculptures seem to have been acquired early in this century, and it is possible, though proof is lacking, that they were found at Deir el-Durunka.

Wood; early XII Dynasty (ca. 2000–1780 B.C.).
Height without base: 24.7 cm.; with base: 27.5 cm.

BIBLIOGRAPHY: Sultan, no. 223, pl. XXXIX.

The Baltimore companion piece is carefully published by Georg Steindorff, Catalogue of the Egyptian Sculpture in the Walters Art Gallery (Baltimore, 1946), no. 79, pl. XIV. The vendor stated that the piece was "from Asyut," but Steindorff thinks it may have been from Meir.　　　　　(J. D. C.)

183   The Singer Imeny

The man depicted in this fine black granite statue is seated on the ground, his feet folded under him. His face is idealized and youthful, but the conventionalized rolls of fat on the torso show the man to be, in fact, no longer young. His left hand is placed on the breast in a gesture of reverence before the gods, who are invoked in the inscription.

The inscription is incised in four lines on the skirt and one line on the top of the base. It is a traditional offering formula, here invoking "Hathor, Mistress of Kusae," the modern Kusiyeh, near Meir, which is probably the area where this sculpture was found. The man was called Imeny and was Director of Singers (not a very high position), presumably in the local temple, though the post could have been completely secular. His father was called Sesi, and, as no title is given for him, he was probably of humble origin.

The inscription on the skirt reads "An offering that the king gives to Hathor, Mistress of Cusae, that she may give offerings of bread and milk, beer, meat and fowl, clothing, incense, oil, and every good and pure thing on which a god lives for the soul of the Director of Singers, Imeny, justified, possessor of reverence." The inscription on top of the base reads "Revered before Ptah-Seker, the Director of Singers, Imeny born of Sesi, possessor of reverence."
Before this sculpture was added to the collection in 1964, it was for several decades in a private possession in Cairo.

Stone; XII Dynasty, probably second half of that period.
Height: 29.3 cm.   (J. D. C.)

184 Statuette of a Man

With his left hand held against his upper right arm in a gesture of deference, this standing man wears a long, slightly flaring skirt of a type known since the later Old Kingdom. The skull is pronouncedly ovoid. The front of the feet and the right arm are separate pieces; the left arm is composed of two more, and the hand is still another piece that is pegged in place. Painted areas are the kilt, whose white pigment is largely lost; the base, originally blue but now black; the black eyebrows; and the eyes, which are white and black. The nose is rubbed and the rectangular base is lost – otherwise the object is intact.

The single column of incised inscription down the front of the skirt is filled with blue pigment and is poorly cut. It reads "Honored before Ptah-Seker, the Steward, ... Aper-hen." The first sign of the man's name is so poorly cut that the reading given here can only be considered tentative. The invocation to Ptah suggests a Memphite origin, but this is by no means certain.

Wood, XII Dynasty; probably late in that period.
Height without base: 28 cm.

BIBLIOGRAPHY: Sultan, no. 223, pl. XXXV.

(J. D. C.)

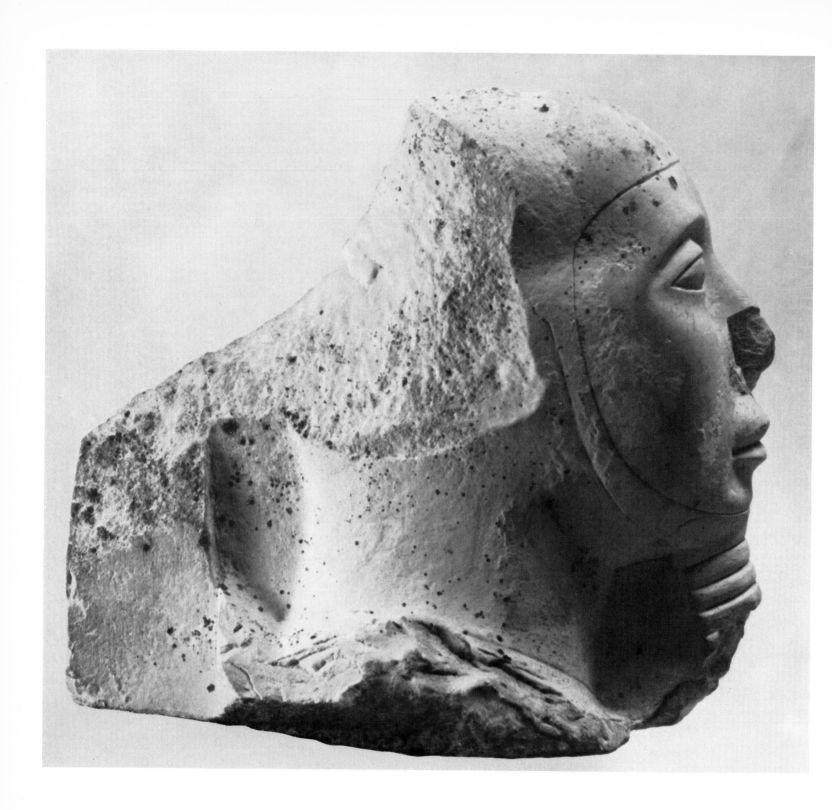

185 Head of the God Ptah

A sculpture of great rarity, this fragment is from a temple statue of a deity made in the Middle Kingdom. That it represents the god Ptah is made certain by the close fitting caplike headdress, which in early times was peculiar to this deity. A strap supports the divine beard, but only the spring of the right shoulder survives. This is the earliest known likeness of Ptah in the round in Egyptian art. The treatment of the eyes with heavy overlapping upper lids indicates a date within the reigns of Sesostris III and Amenemhet III.

Limestone, XII Dynasty (ca. 2000–1780 B.C.).
Height: 17.5 cm.; depth: 19.5 cm.

BIBLIOGRAPHY: Earl Ertman, Journal of Near Eastern Studies, 31 (April 1972), pp. 83–86. (J. D. C.)

186 Female Offering Bearer

In this wooden statuette, a woman bearing offerings stands frontally on a rectangular base. The composition follows a well-known type with a box balanced on the head and the right hand clasping a duck (of which only the wings survive). The dress is supported by straps over the shoulders, which leave the breasts exposed. The feet are together on a small base that is inserted into a larger base. Both statue and base are of relatively soft wood.

The painted areas are: the lappet wig (blue), the close-clinging dress (white – much of this paint now lost), flesh areas (yellow), toenails (white – the fingernails were not painted, as they did not show), top of box (white with black lines on the sides), the plastic eyebrows (black), the eyes (white and black), and the base (a light pink-red).

In general, the sculpture follows a formula well established in the Middle Kingdom, but it has considerable variation in detail. Indeed, it has not been possible to tie this work down to a particular site, even though numerous comparable offering-bearer statuettes are known. For example, the lappet wig seems unknown in the Assiut area.

Wood; XII Dynasty.
Height (without base): 33 cm.; height of base: 3.7 cm.

BIBLIOGRAPHY: Sultan, no. 221, pl. XXXIV.   (J. D. C.)

187   Statuette of a Concubine

This statuette of a nude girl standing frontally on a rectangular base is uninscribed. The well-modeled body has the long arms so typical of the XII Dynasty. For decoration the girl wears a striated or braided wig painted black (perhaps originally blue) with lappets falling on to her shoulders. Between these lappets is a three-strand necklace, u-shaped, with black, red, and green beads. Her bracelets are formed of red and green beads outlined in black, but her anklets are entirely black. She wears sandals that have white soles and black tie strings. Her nipples are painted black, as is the pubic area. Other painted areas are the base (red over a white ground), finger and toenails (white), eyebrows (in relief, black), and eyes (white and black with small touches of red at the outer ends). The statue is made of a fairly hard wood of compact texture with no visible graining. Its surface seems to have been painted yellow. Curiously enough, the base is also made of hard wood.

This sculpture was found in the tomb of the Overseer of the Seal, Nakht, at Deir el-Durunka in Chassinat's excavations. Comparable pieces, some of them inscribed, were found at the same time. All of them appear to have been intended as companions of the dead.

Wood; XII Dynasty.
Height, exclusive of base: 31.5 cm.; height of base: 3 cm.

BIBLIOGRAPHY: E. Chassinat and C. Palanque, "Une campagne de fouilles dans la nécropole d'Assiout," in MIFAOC vol. 24, (Cairo 1911), pl. XXVII, p. 135; Sultan, no. 226, pl. XXXVII; J. Vandier, Manuel d'archéologie égyptienne, vol. 3, La Statuaire (Paris, 1958), p. 157, pl. LV, no. 3.   (J. D. C.)

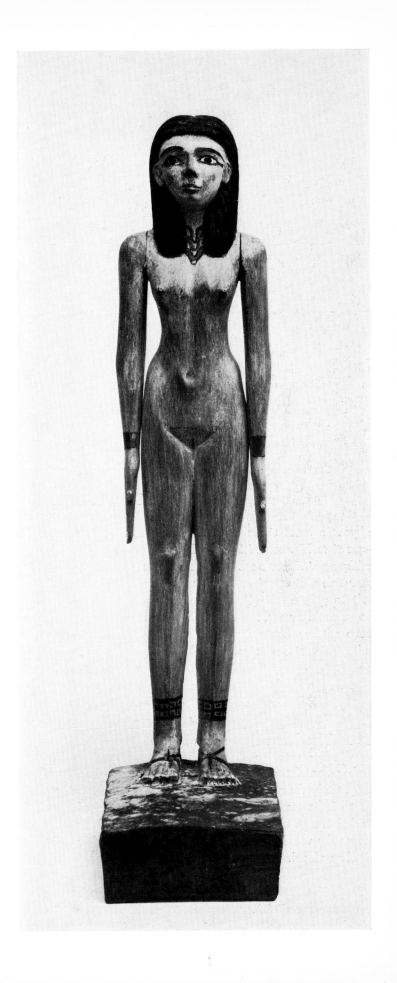

189 Head of a Foreigner

Perhaps a prisoner, wearing a headdress with a plain circular area at its top, the front only being braided. The slanting eyes, prominent cheekbones and deep furrows running down from the nose are realistic details frequently found in Egyptian representations of foreigners.

Yellow limestone; late XVIII Dynasty (ca. 1400–1340 B.C.); Height: 6.1 cm.

BIBLIOGRAPHY: Akhenaton, no. 95.   (J. D. C.)

188 Head and Torso of a Lady

A fragment from a wooden statuette of a standing lady. Only the right half of the head and adjoining part of the torso are preserved. A band decorated with lotus petals encircles the long wig. The lady wears the usual elaborately pleated dress. Probably Theban school.

Wood; XIX Dynasty, probably reign of Horemheb (ca. 1340–1300 B.C.).
Height: 13 cm.   (J. D. C.)

190 Decorated Cover

A cover in light brown wood with a relief of an ibex kneeling on a basket (the neb-sign). The holes were originally supplied with knobs, the upper one serving as a swivel, the lower one when bound with cord forming a lock. The cover could belong either to a cylindrical box or to a shallow bowl used for cosmetics. These bowls were often of another material.

This subject, a kneeling ibex with or without a *neb*-sign, first appeared in Egyptian art in Dynasty XVIII and quickly occupied an important place in the decorative arts. It is an unusual composition and almost certainly had some ideographic or symbolic meaning such as 'all subject peoples' but the precise meaning is elusive. The composition appears, among other places, on the sides of an armchair of Queen Tiye in combination with magical symbols and, much later, on the great leather funerary canopy of Queen Isetemkhebi of Dynasty XXI where it is in the company of other decorations all with amuletic significance. It is but reasonable to suppose that this composition also had amuletic value as yet undetermined. Numerous other examples could be quoted.

Wood; late XVIII Dynasty (ca. 1400–1340 B.C.).
Diameter: 10.3 cm.

BIBLIOGRAPHY: Kayser, p. 314, fig. 293; Akhenaten, fig. 96.
(J. D. C.)

191 Sacrificial Dish

It may be presumed that this small dish with spout was used for pouring liquid over offerings in the process of making a sacrifice to a deity or a deceased person. It is made of Egyptian alabaster with remarkably thin walls and a small circular opening leading to the long spout. The workmanship is excellent, as is the condition, but the date of manufacture is uncertain. The type is clearly later Old Kingdom, but the extreme delicacy of the object also makes an even later date possible, for in the Ptolemaic and Roman periods, the Egyptians made stone vessels of a fineness that rivaled blown glass.

Alabaster; probably late Old Kingdom but possibly Ptolemaic period.
Diameter: 8.5 cm.   (J. D. C.)

192   Magical or Medical Vessel

Recently, Emma Brunner-Traut completed her study of related alabaster vases, including this one that is in the form of a seated woman. Here, as in many of the other examples in the group, the headdress terminates in back in a large lotus flower in profile. Above the lotus are the remains of a handle, which originally was joined to the rim. The right hand clutches a horn that ends in a small spoon. The obese body and epicene features are typical of these vessels.

Dr. Brunner-Traut believes that these vessels were used by women as magical vessels, the contents to be rubbed against the body during pregnancy.

Alabaster; late XVIII Dynasty or slightly later.
Height: 13.3 cm.

BIBLIOGRAPHY: Recueil de Travaux, 22 (1900), pp. 65 ff., pls. I–III; Forman Collection, Sale Catalogue, Sotheby (London, June 1899), no. 235; MacGregor Collection, Sale Catalogue, Sotheby (London, 1922), no. 1003; M. A. Murray, Historical Studies, 2, pl. XXIV, no. 47; E. Brunner-Traut, "Gravidenflasche" in: Archäologie und altes Testament, Festschrift für Kurt Galling (Tübingen, 1970), pp. 35–48.   (J. D. C.)

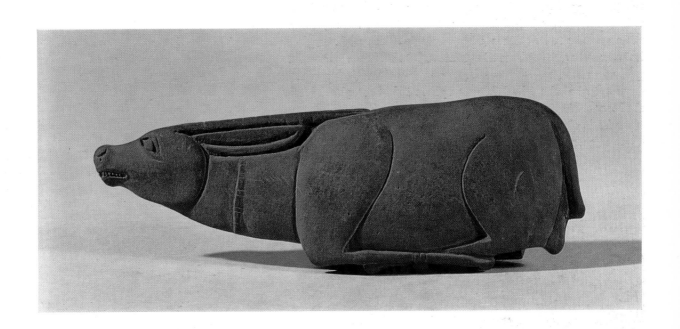

193 Toilet Tray

Originally blue, the surface of this molded toilet tray in the form of a bound oryx has turned into a green matte finish, as so often happens with this medium. A thin collar is incised around the neck. The mouth is open, revealing all the teeth, a detail that is unusual in most Egyptian art except representations of animals and foreigners. Within the container area is a small battered mass, the remains of a small frog in the round, a playful touch known only in a few other examples.

Egyptian blue; late XVIII Dynasty (ca. 1417–1390 B.C.).
Length: 13 cm.

BIBLIOGRAPHY: Sultan, no. 674, pls. LXXXI and LXXXII.

(J. D. C.)

194 Jug

A jug with ovoid body and cylindrical neck, unusual in that the neck is fluted both on the interior and exterior. The rim is partly restored in the area adjoining the handle.

Alabaster; XVIII Dynasty (ca. 1570–1340 B.C.).
Height: 20.3 cm.

BIBLIOGRAPHY: Kayser, fig. 41. (J. D. C.)

195 Tomb Painting

Two priests, one with a liturgical papyrus, the other with censer and holy water, stand in the funeral barge chanting and censing as the body of Nebamun is carried to the Theban necropolis. From the west wall of the tomb chapel of Nebamun at Thebes.

XVIII Dynasty (1400–1390 B.C.).
Height: 15.6 cm.

BIBLIOGRAPHY: Metropolitan Museum Exhib. Cat., no. 75. (J. D. C.)

196 Tomb Painting

The king's chief sculptor Nebamun is shown offering
to the gods. From the south wall of his tomb chapel at
Thebes. There are scattered areas of repainting on the
head.

XVIII Dynasty (1400–1390 B.C.).
Height: 35.7 cm.

BIBLIOGRAPHY: N. de Garis Davies, Metropolitan Museum of Art Exped., vol. IV, 1925, pls. 3–8; André
Lhote, Les chefs d'œuvre de la Peinture Egyptienne, fig.
24; Metropolitan Museum Exhib. Cat., no. 76.

(J. D. C.)

197 Game of Senet

Pale blue-green faience draught-board of thirty squares made and fired in one piece. The five squares at the lower right are inscribed, but their interpretation is much disputed. There are twenty separate draught-pieces, also in faience. The board has been glazed on all surfaces, including the base, but the right end appears to have been abraded or deliberately cut down. Found in the Tanis area.

Faience; XVIII–XIX Dynasty (ca. 1570–1200 B.C.).
Height: 3.3 cm.; length: 33.5 cm.

BIBLIOGRAPHY: Kayser, fig. 129; a comprehensive discussion of these thirty-square boards was made by W. Needler, The Journal of Egyptian Archaeology 39 (1953), 60 ff.   (J. D. C.)

198 Perfume Container

A toilet spoon in the form of a naked girl swimming and holding in her outstretched hands a fish-shaped dish (the *bulti* fish), its cover now lost. Around the girl's neck is a wide collar necklace (wesekh-necklace). As always, the head was made separately and has a braided wig with plain band. The body is excellently modelled, with the pubic triangle clearly delineated and having registers of short incisions to indicate hair.

Wood; XVIII Dynasty, reign of Amenhotep III (ca. 1400–1380 B.C.). Length: 23.7 cm.

BIBLIOGRAPHY: Kayser, p. 317, fig. 297; Ingrid Wallert, Der verzierte Löffel, seine Formgeschichte und Verwendung im alten Ägypten, (Wiesbaden, 1967), p. 134, no. 22 and pl. 12; Bulletin of the Cleveland Museum of Art, February, 1973, v. LX, no. 2, p. 50, fig. 13 and p. 49.
(J. D. C.)

199   Cosmetic Tray

A dish in the form of a cartouche with the usual binding at the base here interspersed with two lotus blossoms. The incised bowl area is decorated with an elaborate composition of a clump of papyrus rising from the water. On two upper papyrus umbels, two birds sit on nests, a composition dating back as far as the Old Kingdom. Below this are two flowers: the right, apparently a marguerite, or corn flower, is seen in top view; the left, a starlike flower, is too conventionalized to identify. Below the flowers is a clump of three lotus blossoms and three buds, which are behind a large bulti-fish in profile. Two small birds, irregularly placed, complete the composition. A rectangular handle below the binding of the cartouche is decorated in high relief, which shows a seated duckling and, behind it, a group consisting of a lotus flower and buds.

While the dish is sufficiently sturdy for actual use, it was probably intended as funerary equipment, as were the majority of comparable pieces in wood. It shows no trace of wear or actual use.

Stone; XVIII Dynasty (probably reign of Amenhotep III).
Length: 13 cm.

Bibliography: Sale Catalogue, D. David-Weill Collection (Hotel Drouot, Paris, June 16, 1971), no. 4.   (J. D. C.)

200   A Bronze Weight (?)

An alert frog rests in the usual composition with the rear legs folded, the head erect, and seated on a lotus leaf, a pose constantly repeated in nature in almost every country in the world. Substitute a pond lily leaf for the lotus and the subject could be duplicated endlessly in many areas.

One cannot be certain, but probably this charming object served as an object of daily use, perhaps a weight. As with all small metal objects in Egypt it was cast solid.

Late XVIII Dynasty.
Diameter of base: 2.5 by 2.9 cm.; height: 1.8 cm.   (J. D. C.)

201 Kohl Tube

Inscribed upon this ivory kohl tube, in a single column, are the words "the good god, Lord of the Two Lands, Neb-Maat-Re" and "The Princess Isis, may she live." To the right of this inscription, close to the top, is a brief one – probably added slightly later – "Geb endures." Both the inscription column and its enclosing rectangle were filled with Egyptian blue, of which extensive traces remain, but "Geb endures" was never inlaid. Around the rim is a register of lotus petals, each surmounted by a circle alternating with a column of three small rectangles. These details are in sunk relief with small cylindrical holes bored in the floor of each, presumably to insure a better grip for the inlays. Extensive traces survive of the blue and red pigment inlays. About an inch above the base – at about the same level as the floor of the tube – a line was incised around the cylinder.

Kohl tubes with royal inscriptions were made in considerable quantities late in the XVIIIth Dynasty for presentation to courtiers. Usually they bear the name of the reigning monarch and his consort. Coupling the king's name with that of one of his daughters is unusual, but this inscription is almost paralleled on a remarkably similar ivory tube found by Petrie at Medinet Gurob, which is now in the Cairo Museum. Indeed, despite trivial differences in the inscriptions, the two tubes are probably from the same workshop and almost certainly were found in the same excavation.

Virtually nothing is known of this Princess Isis. She seems to have been a child of the king's later years. In addition to the kohl tube already mentioned, she is referred to in the Temple of Soleb, but nothing is known of her life.

The inscription "Geb endures" (if this is the correct reading) is not otherwise recorded, and other readings are possible. Whatever the reading, this brief inscription must contain the name of the owner, though no other example of this custom is known.

Ivory; XVIII Dynasty (late in the reign of Amenhotep III); ca. 1400–1380 B.C. Length: 16.9 cm.; diameter: 2 cm.

BIBLIOGRAPHY: Sultan, no. 534, pls. LXIX and LXX; W. M. F. Petrie, Kahun, Gurob and Hawara (London, 1890), pp. 32, 35; Georges Bénédite, "Objets de toilette," in Catalogue général des antiquités égyptiennes du Musée du Caire (Cairo, 1911), no. 44521, pl. 28. He does not mention either the provenience, or the date of acquisition of the kohl tube published, but it must be the one found by Petrie. It is in fragile condition and seemingly has lost all color. (J. D. C.)

The symbol consists of a protome in the form of a lion's head holding in its open jaws a Negro head. The object was elaborately inlaid and the lion's eyes still retain their original gold linings, which cover the entire eye socket, forming the rims of the eyelids; of their inlays nothing survives.

Originally there were four separately made fanglike gold teeth on each side. Only three remain intact along with one root on the right side. On the left a single root is the sole survivor.

The Negro head is a superb representation of a native of Central Africa with markedly prognathic jaw and heavy lips. Both eyes were outlined and inlaid in gold; unfortunately only the right has been preserved. The mouth, as so often occurs in Egyptian representations of foreigners, is slightly open. Large hoop earrings and a small close fitting cap with three registers of fringes or curls complete the representation of the African.

The roughly circular area at the back of the lion's head is hollowed for attachment to a plug, and on the walls of this area are two slender piercings for the insertion of pins to hold the protome in position. The surface is matte and retains considerable encrustation from long burial.

The protome's original position was horizontal and this example may well have been one of a set of nine, representing the traditional enemies of Egypt. The small scale of the sculpture seems to rule out the possibility that it originally decorated a large piece of furniture. However, it is possible that it was a decoration placed on a small chest or box, but there is no conclusive evidence on this point. The lion no doubt represents the King of Egypt, while the whole composition is a symbol both of Egypt's absolute control over her enemies and her ability to crush them without warning.

As the object is known to be from Qantir in the eastern Delta, a city apparently founded by Ramesses II of Dynasty XIX, a date within this dynasty would be expected. However, the excellence of the work, its great quality and style virtually demand a date within the reign of Amenhotep III, which is where the writer prefers to place it. As it is well established that Ramesses II shifted sculptures from all over Egypt to his newly founded Delta sites, it is not difficult to suppose that he also removed temple and palace furnishings from Thebes and Memphis to decorate his northern centers. This would explain the finding of an earlier object at a Dynasty XIX site.

Egyptian blue (light); probably late XVIII Dynasty, reign of Amenhotep III.
Length: 4.2 cm.; height: 2.85 cm.

(J. D. C.)

203 Kohl Container

With cylindrical openings that run almost the entire height of the vessel, this quadruple container for kohl is of mottled gray, brown, and black serpentine. The flat swivel cover is pinkish, crystalline limestone and is held in place by a brown wooden applicator.
The object shows no trace of wear or use and apparently was made for funerary purposes.

Serpentine, limestone; XVIII Dynasty.
Height with cover: 7.7 cm.; length of applicator (incomplete): 6.7 cm.

(J. D. C.)

204 Kohl Jar

Undecorated, the body of this traditionally shaped kohl jar is translucent. It is carved in one piece with its stand, and has a separate disk cover with the usual boss on the under surface to prevent the cover from sliding. It has a matte surface and is intact. There is the usual cylindrical opening within the body.

Marble (anhydrite); probably early XVIII Dynasty.
Height with cover: 6.3 cm.; diameter of cover: 4.4 cm.   (J. D. C.)

205 Head of a Foreigner

This limestone head, which is apparently from a temple sculpture, probably represents a Syrian. Both headdress and beard are striated in a somewhat un-Egyptian style. Extensive traces of black paint survive on the headdress and beard, while the face and body retain scatterings of dark red paint. The crinkled surface, particularly of the skin areas, is most exceptional; it implies that the sculpture was buried in an unusual environment.

Survival of a small part of the spring of the left shoulder suggests that this piece was a representation of a bound and kneeling foreign captive. A slight downward cast of the eyes supports this suggestion. Formerly in the collection of the Textile Museum, Washington, D.C., this sculpture was first known in the Cairo art trade in the 1930s. Similar compositions are known from the later Old Kingdom.

Limestone; late XVIII Dynasty – early XIX Dynasty.
Height: 11.7 cm.

(J. D. C.)

206 Head of a Princess

This small girl's head is ivory that has turned yellow and become glossy; it retains no trace of paint. Her idealized features show no individuality. There are two long flesh folds in the neck, a fortunate indication of date. Various details of construction clearly indicate that this tiny head is from a composite statuette, very probably representing one of the daughters of Amenhotep III.

The top of the head is finished on a diagonal that slopes down to the back. Toward the rear of this slope is a relatively large circular hole for attaching the headdress, or wig, probably of faience. Just below where ears would be, on the viewer's right, are two small holes for attaching details of braids or of the crown. On the opposite side of the face is a single small hole. On the base of the neck is another opening for a rod, which served as an attachment to the body.

When complete with parts in faience, glass, and semi-precious stones, these miniature composite sculptures (probably made only in royal workshops), must have been glittering trifles. They were probably used about the palaces much as we use photographs; upon the death of major members of the royal family they formed part of the funerary equipment.

Ivory; late XVIII Dynasty (probably reign of Amenhotep III).
Height: 2.7 cm.

BIBLIOGRAPHY: Sultan, no. 553, pl. LXIX, center, left.　　　　　(J. D. C.)

207　Miniature Cube Statuette

This small, green serpentine sculpture of a man seated on a base, slightly rounded at the back, is uninscribed. The body is completely enveloped in a great cloak with the body contours well indicated. The man's hands, which emerge from the dress, are clenched, empty, and are placed flat. He wears a double wig; the upper one is plain, the lower curled. The face is idealized; the eyebrows are not indicated, and only the lower tips of the ears are shown. There is a substantial open space between the chin and body.

Serpentine; XVIII Dynasty – early XIX Dynasty (or archaising work of XXVI Dynasty).
Height: 4.8 cm.　　　　　(J. D. C.)

208 Head of a King

This conventionalized profile of a king facing left is from an inlay figure composed of various materials. The features are so impersonal that there is little evidence for dating, but the absence of piercing in the ear and of flesh folds in the neck suggests a date before the latter part of the reign of Amenhotep III. The object may even antedate his reign. The surface is highly polished.

Red jasper; XVIII (?) Dynasty.
Height: 4.5 cm.   (J. D. C.)

209 Isis and Horus

In this traditional composition, the goddess Isis is holding Horus. She is frontally poised, her legs in the round. Horus is nude, with his hands at his sides. Isis wears the Vulture headdress with two uraei, each with a disk and a set of horns. On the top of her head is a modius with a circular opening on its top surface, presumably for the insertion of an attribute. The right hand and arm of Isis, which supported her breast, are lost. The sculpture is broken at the waist.

The throne has the usual scale pattern on the sides. There is a heavy loop at the back of the modius. On the base is an opening square in section, which is about 2.5 cm. in depth. It is obviously connected with the molding of this object but its specific function is not apparent. The interior of the object is bright blue and granular in composition. The exterior surface is very compact, gray-blue in color, with a low polish. This is an extremely fine example of sculpture in Egyptian blue, a material closely allied to glass.

Egyptian blue; XVIII Dynasty (probably reign of Amenhotep III); ca. 1400–1379 B.C.
Height: 6.2 cm.

From the Omar Pasha Sultan Collection.   (J. D. C.)

210 Portrait of a King

At about the same time that the great cache of Amarna reliefs was first discovered at Hermopolis Magna, on the west bank of the Nile, this head was also found there. It is an impressive piece of royal sculpture: it is over lifesize and made of fine crystalline limestone of the sort reserved for royal work.

At first glance, it shows no obvious similarity to any previously recognized royal portrait. After no more than a cursory examination, however, it seems possible to limit the date of the sculpture. The great sensitivity of the face and, in particular, the fleshly treatment of the eyes, with their heavy, soft upper eyelids, suggest a work of the Amarna Period. The absence of the more striking characteristics of that period implies that this is a product of the time when the new style was on the wane, roughly between 1365 and 1345 B.C. Within those two decades, there were five Egyptian kings: Akhenaten, Smenkhkare, Tutankhamen, Ay, and Horemheb, who was the last king of the XVIII Dynasty.

The features of Akhenaten, Tutankhamen, and Horemheb are so well known that it is apparent this sculpture does not depict any one of them. We have no idea of the appearance of Smenkhkare, but it is only reasonable to suppose that if this head represented him it would have more conspicuous characteristics of the developed Amarna style. Thus, by elimination, Ay seems the most probable candidate.

The surviving, certainly identified portraits of Ay seem to have been produced by two separate schools: one dominated by an idealizing trend, the other dominated by realism. This sculpture seems clearly of the idealizing school, and it is perhaps most closely related to the well-known relief of Ay now in Boston.

Although it could be plausibly argued that this sculpture can be identified with Ramesses II because the fleshly treatment of the eyes is a characteristic occasionally found in certain large-scale representations of him, I believe that the introspective and brooding qualities of this portrait are incompatible with XIX Dynasty style and are more characteristic of the late XVIII Dynasty. Thus, Ay, could be the individual represented.

Limestone; probably late XVIII Dynasty; ca. 1352–1348 B.C.
Height: 34.2 cm.

BIBLIOGRAPHY: My discussion of this sculpture, prepared at an earlier date, will appear in a forthcoming issue of Antike Welt. (J. D. C.)

211   Bes as Attendant

This frontally poised, standing figure of the god Bes is cream-colored faience with a headdress of gray-blue. The lion skin is pale yellow with dark brown spots. Bes's arms are extended, clasping a ring of the same cream color as his body and banded with gray-blue. Under his feet is a square base.

The ring is a support for an applicator. The rectangular container on his head is hollow. Its walls show traces of a blue substance, which is, clearly, the residue of kohl or some other cosmetic. Apparently the god was represented presenting an applicator to the owner, and at the same time storing an essential cosmetic. While utensils in the form of this deity are fairly frequent, parallels of Bes supporting an applicator are not known. Bes was the lone god among Egyptian deities engaged exclusively in terrestrial activities.

Faience; early XIX Dynasty ca. 1320–1280 B.C.
Height: 9 cm.; width: 4.4 cm.

BIBLIOGRAPHY: Sultan no. 186, pl. XXXI; J. Vandier-d'Abbadie, Les objets de toilette égyptiennes au Musée du Louvre (Paris, 1972), nos. 164, 160, 172, etc.   (J. D. C.)

212   Heads of Foreigners

The upper head represents a Negro, the lower, a Syrian. They seem to have been broken from bodies. They were made separately to be inlaid on rectangular tiles, which were intended as architectural decoration. Both heads are glazed only on the top surface. They have very coarse-grained faience bodies.

The surface of the Negro head is now very worn and green but was originally black and glossy. The eye is a separate inlay of opaque white stone while the pupil is an unidentified black substance. Apparently, the large hoop earring was inlaid separately. The head of the Syrian was also glazed only on the top surface, which is now entirely matte. His flesh is cream color; the beard and moustache are painted black. On the neck are cords painted in red. The eyes, now lost, were separate inlays. In Egyptian art, the open mouth is a detail that is restricted to representations of foreigners and animals.

Faience; XIX or XX Dynasty.
Negro, width: 7 cm.; Syrian, height: 7.1 cm.   (J. D. C.)

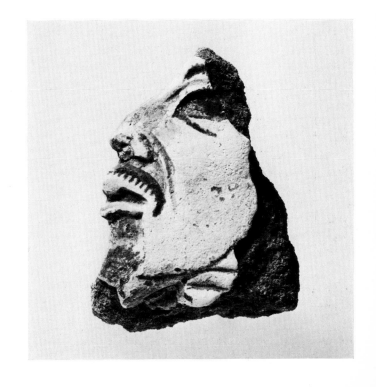

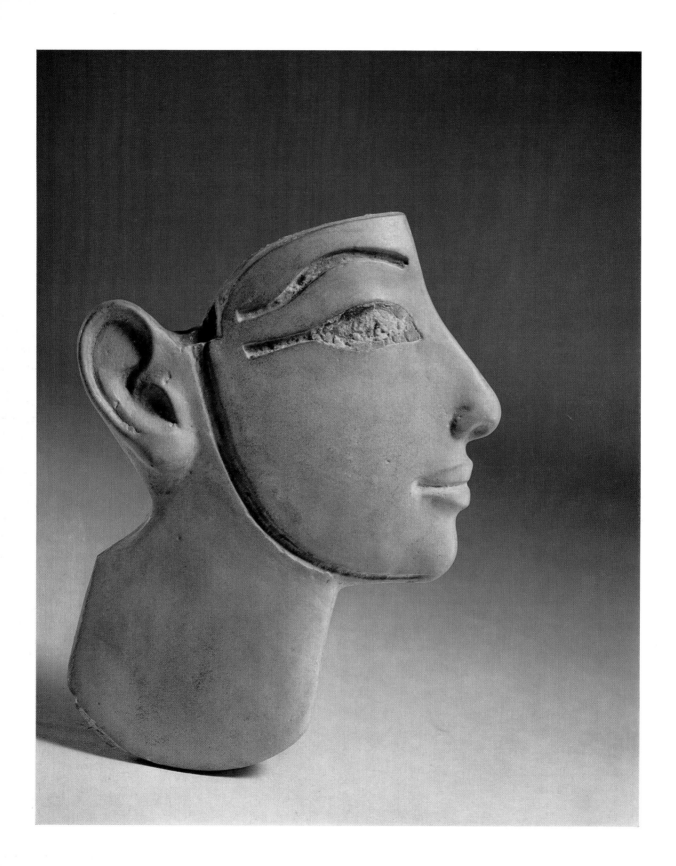

213 Royal Inlay Head

This pale green-blue faience head had an eye outlined in dark (?) blue glass: its center is now white but the material is decayed and unidentified. The eyebrow and beard strap were doubtless also inlaid in dark blue glass. The body of the faience is exceptionally dense, very like stone. Its surface is highly compact and lustrous, strongly suggesting porcelain.

The angle of this head clearly indicates that it is from the standing figure of a king bending deferentially toward a deity to whom he offers gifts. The completed figure was composed of various materials, a fact that points to an origin in the XVIII Dynasty.

While there are earlier examples of jewelry in which inlaid figures are assembled from various semi-precious stones, as transferred to temple walls and large objects, the technique is known only from the late XVIII Dynasty. That it continued into later times has never previously been established, but the composition of the faience seems to provide incontrovertible evidence for assigning the head a late date. Such a substance is unknown before a very late date. In style this face could belong anywhere from the mid XVIII Dynasty to a late Dynasty, for it is of an idealizing cast that never entirely left Egyptian art during this long stretch of time. But the composition of the faience leaves no doubt. The only other inlay of comparable function and date is a head in opaque red glass now in the Corning Museum. In the absence of similar examples, its date has always been uncertain. Both pieces were probably inlaid into a wooden naos, which contained the cult statue of the god. The figure published here was on the (spectator's) left side of the naos facing the door.

Faience and glass; late Dynastic Period.
Height: 13 cm.; diagonal measurement: 15.5 cm.; thickness: 2.5 cm.

BIBLIOGRAPHY: Sultan, no. 678, pls. LXXX, LXXXI, and LXXXIII. The Corning head is published in several places, among them R. W. Smith, Glass from the Ancient World (Corning, N. Y., 1957), no. 32 (illustrated).   (J. D. C.)

214 Architectural Tile

Only the top surface of this faience tile is glazed. The cartouche and all the elements of the name, Ramesses IV, are in relief; they are white on a gray background. The body of the faience is highly granular and light brown in color. Doubtless for a temple, this tile was assembled from five pieces.

The reading of Ramesside cartouches is frequently a complex affair. If this one is indeed that of Ramesses IV, the tile is a rarity. This king had a reign of only about six years, during which he completed few large architectural constructions except his tomb. Some projects were started, though not completed, at Thebes. Obviously, the inlaying of glazed tiles would be among the finishing touches applied to any building, though it is possible that the tile was made in anticipation of ultimate use.

Faience; XX Dynasty, reign of Ramesses IV; ca. 1166–1160 B.C.
Height: 12.5 cm.; width: 6 cm.
From the Omar Pasha Sultan Collection. (J. D. C.)

215 Necklace Terminals

Necklace terminals were traditionally shaped like falcons' heads, as here. This pair is light blue faience, glazed on all surfaces. The circular eye was incised before firing, as was the conventional horizontal drop under the eye. Each terminal is pierced seven times along the base and lower back. In the absence of documentation, terminals of this type are particularly difficult to date, as the type hardly changed over the centuries.

Faience; Middle Kingdom (?) or Late Period (?).
Width at base: 6.9 cm.
From the Omar Pasha Sultan Collection. (J. D. C.)

216 Horus Falcon

This Horus falcon inlay in faience (facing left) is, as always, represented in an entirely traditional manner. The faience has a light green-blue, compact body. The wing feathers are light and dark green-blue, and are outlined in lighter green-blue. Other areas of the body are monochrome green-blue. The eye appears to be a black inlay. Doubtless, this object is from a royal titulary, which had been inlaid in the walls of a naos or some similar chamber. The falcon stood on the hieroglyphic sign for gold, thus introducing the Golden Horus name for a king.

Comparable examples, in the same fine faience, have long been in the Metropolitan Museum. The feet are missing, and the beak area is restored.

Faience; late Dynastic.
Height: 8.7 cm.
From the Omar Pasha Sultan Collection.   (J. D. C.)

217   Shawabti of Huy

This traditional shawabti, depicts "The Chief of Weighing, or Measuring, Huy, justified." He is painted white and wears a black double wig and a large *wesekh* collar in yellow, red, black, and blue. He clasps the customary hoe and pick, both yellow. His flesh is very dark red, his eyes are white and black, and his ear lobes are pierced. Around the body are seven lines of incised inscription, the traditional shawabti formula, painted black and enclosed within red lines. On the front of the feet are three short columns of text. The title "Chief of Weighing or Measuring" is somewhat unusual. For the correct reading I am indebted to Professor Hans Goedicke of Johns Hopkins University. Huy was probably a minor official in a commissary where he supervised the precise weighing or measuring of supplies issued to workers. This glorification of trivial offices, typical of the old Orient, was especially common in Egypt with its vast bureaucracy.

Wood; from Deir el-Medina; Ramesside (?) or earlier.
Height: 21 cm.   (J. D. C.)

218   Panel of a Shrine

This soft wood panel is flanged on each end
for attachment to a shrine. In high relief, on
the front face, is a *djed*-column, the ancient
symbol of Osiris. Atop the column sits an
atef-crown, one of the major and most typical
of those worn by Osiris.

Cynocephalus apes, the sacred animals of
Thoth, flank this motif. The panel was excavated at Tuna el-Gebel, chief shrine of Thoth.

Wood; Ptolemaic Period; probably third-sec-
ond century B.C.

Height: 22 cm.; width: 10 cm.   (J. D. C.)

219 The God Harpocrates

A splendid representation of this famous deity, the son of Isis and Osiris, this statuette shows him seated, with his left arm by his side; his right hand was originally at his mouth.

Inlaid in gold around his neck is a *wesekh* necklace. Underneath it, in silver, is a single cord supporting a gold adaptation of the curious double amulet, never satisfactorily explained, found on royal sculptures of the late XII Dynasty. The right arm was cast separately and dowled in place; the remainder was cast solid in one piece. On the right side of the head is a square opening for a sidelock or – if this bronze was part of a group sculpture – for attachment to Isis. The surface, now a lustrous, medium green of great beauty, has doubtless been polished in the present century.

The close fitting cap, at an early date peculiar to Ptah, is shared by several deities in the Late Period, particularly in bronze statuettes. The archaizing detail of the double amulet also suggests a relatively early date, but, since virtually all representations of Harpocrates are of very late date, a Ptolemaic origin is probable.

Bronze, gold, and silver; Late Dynastic to Ptolemaic Period.
Height: 9 cm.

BIBLIOGRAPHY: Johannes Sieveking, Die Bronzen der Sammlung Loeb (Munich, 1913), p. 2, pl. 2.   (J. D. C.)

220 Horus Falcon

This falcon, standing frontally on a small rectangular base, is of traditional type; it is cast solid. The feathers are inlaid in gold, as is the four-strand necklace on the breast. The legs are not decorated. Although the top of the head is overlaid with a small sheet of gold, there is no trace of an attached disk or other similar attribute.

That the gold inlay is indeed ancient (and not a modern insertion as is so frequently the case) is indicated by the traces of cuprite and other minerals that frequently overlap the gold. The piece presumably served as a votive offering. From the Levi de Benzion Collection, Cairo.

Bronze and gold; said to be from Benha (Athribis) in the Delta; late Dynastic – Ptolemaic Period.
Height: 4.8 cm.   (J. D. C.)

221 Finger Ring

Clearly a copy from metal, this intact, dark blue-green faience ring has a very lustrous surface. Each end of the carinated shank terminates in an openwork lotus flower in profile. In turn these flowers support a scarabeus with curved body.

Faience; late XVIII Dynasty (ca. 1400–1380 B.C.).
Diameter: 2.4 cm.
From the Omar Pasha Sultan Collection.   (J. D. C.)

222 Cylindrical Ring

Three squatting deities are represented facing, not each other, but the upper rim of this fine openwork ring in blue faience with a highly lustrous glaze. One, Thoth, with disk and horns, clasps a *was*-scepter. Next is Horus, who wears the Double Crown and also clasps a *was*-scepter. Then comes a goddess, apparently Isis or Hathor, who holds a staff formed of lotus flowers in profile. This object is a type occasionally found in wood. Just below the rim that the deities face is a register of three examples of the hieroglyph for n. It is unlikely that these cylindrical rings were intended for wearing.

Faience; probably from Tuna el-Gebel; probably XXI–XXII Dynasties (ca. 1085–730 B.C.).
Height: 2 cm.; diameter: 2.3 cm.
From the Omar Pasha Sultan Collection.   (J. D. C.)

223 Amulet

An intact openwork cowrie shell in light green faience rests on an undecorated flat base. The central area of the convex upper surface is occupied by a seated cynocephalus ape facing right. In front of him is the feather of Maat reading "truth." Below is an openwork register that surmounts an openwork lotus flower. On each side of the cowrie is an erect uraeus serpent on a lotus flower. At the top is a disk with embracing wings.
A duplicate of the shell is in The Metropolitan Museum of Art. The type persisted until a late date, for still another, which bears the cartouche of Apries of the XXVI Dynasty, is in the Freer Gallery of Art in Washington (unpublished).

Faience; probably from Tuna el-Gebel; probably XXII Dynasty; ca. 935–730 B.C.
Length: 3.9 cm.
From the Omar Pasha Sultan Collection.   (J. D. C.)

224 Openwork Bead

This intact openwork, rectangular, spacer bead in blue-green faience is of a well-known but relatively rare type. It is pierced top and bottom seven times, and its interior surfaces are not glazed. On the center of the obverse is a standing king facing right; he clasps the shoulder of a bound and kneeling Negro captive and presents him to Sakhmet at the right. In her lifted right hand she holds a sistrum, in her left a drooping lotus. Behind the king stands the goddess Mut wearing the Double Crown. She clasps the same insignia as Sakhmet. At each end of the composition is an erect uraeus serpent on a lotus, one with the crown of Upper Egypt, the other with the crown of Lower Egypt.

At the center of the reverse, facing right, Isis stands offering her breast to the child Horus who is on a small stool. On either side of this scene is a kneeling, winged deity, each with disk and apparently animal-headed. Within each pair of wings and flanking the middle area of the central section is a *shen*-sign. Along the upper edge are two horizontal and one vertical illegible cartouches.

While these beads are always called spacers, it is not at all clear how they were used; it seems improbable that they were elements of necklaces.

Faience; probably from Tuna el-Gebel; XXI–XXII Dynasty (ca. 1085–730 B.C.).
Length: 4.2 cm.

BIBLIOGRAPHY: G. A. D. Tait, Journal of Egyptian Archaeology 49 (1963), pp. 93 ff., and in particular p. 130 and pl. XXIV.
From the Omar Pasha Sultan Collection.   (J. D. C.)

225 Amulet

Recumbent on a rectangular base, this cat in dark blue, glossy faience has her head turned at a right angle to her body. At the center of her body are two suckling kittens, and below her head is a suspension loop glazed purple-brown.

Length: 3.8 cm.

BIBLIOGRAPHY: Sultan, no. 153.   (J. D. C.)

Faience; Ptolemaic Period; 330–30 B.C.

226 Amuletic Spacer Bead

All surfaces of this spacer are glazed dark blue. On a rectangular base, which is pierced three times, three cats in the round are seated frontally. The bead is almost certainly an element from a bracelet and was probably separated from its companion pieces by small globular beads.

Length: 4 cm.

BIBLIOGRAPHY: Sultan no. 196 and pl. XXVI.   (J. D. C.)

227 and 228 Amulets

227   This falcon-headed, light blue crocodile that supports a large disk with uraeus is a composite deity: Sobk-Horus or Sobk-Re. As in the following example, there is a wall, pierced for suspension, under the head.

Length: 4.5 cm.
From the Omar Pasha Sultan Collection.   (J. D. C.)

Faience; XXX Dynasty early Ptolemaic Period; ca. 350–250 B.C.

228   A crocodile in light blue, highly lustrous faience represents the god Sobk. One end of the base, as well as the animal's tail, curves to the right, an unusual detail. A thin, pierced, wall supports the head. The modeling is exceptionally fine and detailed. This piece offers an excellent demonstration of the ability of the Egyptians to take an essentially ugly body and transform it into a thing of great beauty.

Length: 3.8 cm.   (J. D. C.)

229 A Nubian Girl

Seated on each shoulder of this nude, standing girl in glossy blue faience is a small monkey; another one is against the inside of her slightly advanced left leg. The girl is nursing a nude child. Her black hair is cut in Nubian style: five small clumps, the two side ones of which are pierced; she is apparently a Negress.

At the base of the girl's spine is a crudeley drawn lotus in black, and a suspension loop is at the back of her neck. Although parallels are known and the girl probably represents some sort of fertility charm, it is still unclear just how this statuette was used.

Faience; late Dynastic – Ptolemaic Periods.
Height: 12.5 cm.

Bibliography: Sultan no. 158 and pl. XXVIII.   (J. D. C.)

229 bis Amulet

This translucent pendant or amulet is in the form of a sun globe flanked by uraeus serpents facing in opposite directions. The group rests on a mat traditional in Egyptian jewelry since at least the twelfth Dynasty. The front surface is decorated with groups of four incised vertical lines. The bodies of the serpents are notched and rest on the circumference of the globe, where they join. Both the obverse and reverse of the circumference are sharply convex. The form of the central portion has traditionally been described as a sun disc. However, about a decade ago Mme. Desroches-Nobelcourt pointed out that the existence of a convex form seemed to indicate that the Egyptians conceived of the sun as a globe. Therefore, in view of the convex structure of this amulet, it is here described as a globe. On the center of the reverse is a notched horizontal loop of cylindrical form, establishing the object as an amulet.

The group presumably represents the sun god Ra protected by the uraeus serpents. While this motif is almost conventional as a decoration of temple lintels, it is rarely known in amulet form. The Schimmel example may well have been the central decoration of a necklace or it may have been part of funerary equipment.

The stone is a fine, cold, gray-blue, which becomes colorless in the area of the serpents. A date far later than that suggested here is indeed possible.

Chalcedony; late XVIII Dynasty (?).
Diameter: 2 cm.; width at serpents' heads: 3.8 cm.

(J. D. C.)

230   Winged Scarab

This piece originally rested on the breast of a mummy and was made, as usual, in three separate pieces. On the central oval plaque is a purple-black scarabeus in relief. The under surface of the plaque is glazed light blue-green. The bright blue wings have feathers in relief, which are outlined in purple-blue, a color repeated at the tips. The standard small area of scale pattern adjoins the place of attachment to the scarab.

The central plate is pierced ten times; each of the wings is pierced eleven times. Pieces of cartonnage or linen still adhere to the under surface.

Faience; probably Ptolemaic Period.
Total wing spread: 26 cm.

BIBLIOGRAPHY: Sultan no. 595, and pls. LXXII and LXXIII.   (J. D. C.)

230 bis   Hedgehog

A hedgehog in medium blue faience, the spines indicated by small black dots painted under the glaze, apparently hollow. The animal is represented rolled into a sphere, a shape he assumes when threatened with danger. The head, in light and dark blue, is in raised relief as are the paws.

The hedgehog, although apparently not a sacred animal, did have magical properties in the Egyptian civilization and representations are frequent particularly in the Middle Kingdom. In the defensive position with its spines erect we can assume an amuletic character for this object. However, the rather cumbersome shape and the absence of a suspension loop argue against this interpretation. It is probably a rattle, though one has to assume that the pellets have disintegrated. Rattles of hedgehog shape, though differing from this example, exist from the Middle Kingdom, an excellent example being in Brooklyn.

Faience; ca. 500 B.C
Diameter: 6 cm.   (J. D. C.)

231   Coffin of a Sacred Cat

A bronze cat, cast hollow with open base. The entire body has been chased with short lines running in different directions to indicate fur. The legs are in the form of half cylinders with only the outer surfaces finished and chased, but why this convention was used is not clear. Very thin tail. An unidentified detail cast between the ears on the top of the head does not appear to be the usual scarab.

Bronze; XXII–XXV Dynasty (?) (ca. 950–660 B.C.).
Height: 47.2 cm.

BIBLIOGRAPHY: Sale Catalogue, Sotheby, London, January 15, 1952, no. 194. Previously in the collection of Lord Powers of Court Castle, Ireland, who seems to have acquired this bronze in Egypt in 1893.   (J. D. C.)

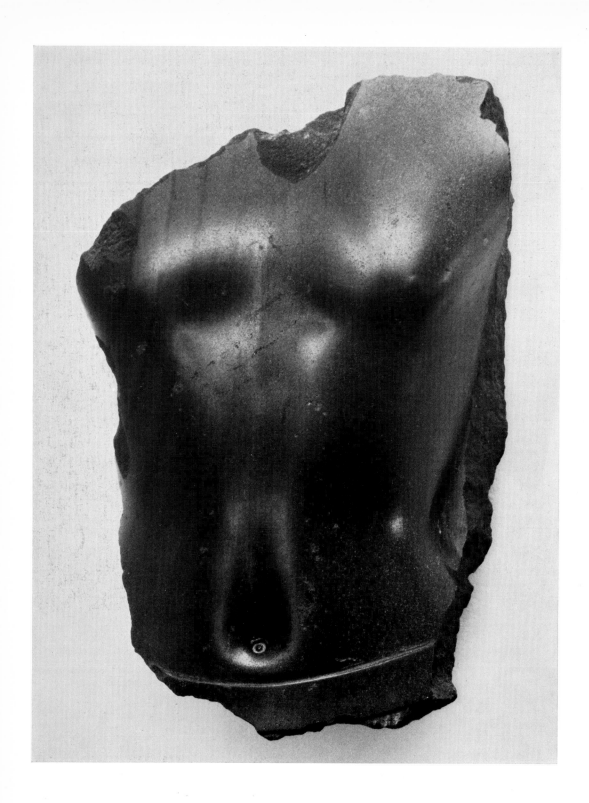

232 Torso

Apparently from a standing statue, this matte-surface fragment is the front half of a male torso. In this conventional composition, the arms, which are not preserved, would have been by the sides.

Basalt (?); XXVI Dynasty to late Dynastic.
Height: 31 cm.   (J. D. C.)

233   Horus Falcon

A bronze falcon, cast hollow, of exceptionally fine workmanship. The legs, which were cast separately, are now lost. Both the feathers and wings were incised, probably as part of the casting process, and afterwards filled with a pigment of light contrasting color. The eyes, apparently original, are of black glass. Of the inlay which surrounded the eyes one piece survives on the left side. It is opaque, jade colored glass. Holes on the top of the head indicate that originally a sun-disk or similar insignia, existed there. The iconography of sacred animals and birds rarely changed over the centuries, and they are thus difficult to date with certainty. The meticulous workmanship and the glass inlays suggest a Saite date. The bronze was doubtless made as a votive offering to the god Horus.

Bronze; XXVI Dynasty (ca. 660–525 B.C.) or slightly later.
Height: 21 cm.   (J. D. C.)

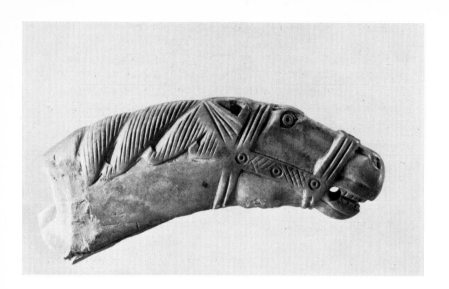

234   Handle in Form of a Horse Head

The head and neck of a horse in the round forming a handle with pistol-like grip. The mane is dressed in conventional braids each terminating in a curl. The mouth is open with the teeth carefully represented. The harness is decorated with small incised circles which are no especial indication of date as they were in use sporadically from the time of the Middle Kingdom.

Representations in the round of horses are decidedly infrequent in Egyptian art and undocumented examples are not easily dated. All indications point to a late date for this specimen which may well have been the handle of a whip. Said to be from the area of Alexandria.

Ivory; Ptolemaic to early Roman Periods.
Length: 10.7 cm.

Bibliography: Formerly MacGregor Collection, no. 678, July 1922, pl. 1.   (J. D. C.)

235   Uraeus Serpent

An example of a well-known type of decorative object fairly common in late Egyptian work. A small scale uraeus serpent with disk has its body erect and frontal, its tail in profile. Cast solid. The body retains its inlays, the upper two being in opaque dark blue glass, the center inlays in opaque red glass while the lowest inlays, now entirely decayed, appear to have been of turquoise blue glass. The entire front surface was gilded traces of which survive. Exceptionally, there are no tenons on the reverse although there is a loop on the back of the head. Substantial numbers of similar pieces have survived, all of late date, but their function has never been established. Possibly they formed friezes on temple equipment but if so it is difficult to explain the loop invariably present on the reverse of the head.

Bronze cast solid; probably Ptolemaic Period.
Height: 9.2 cm.

(J. D. C.)

236 Magical Amulet or Charm

On a rectangular base, a nude, pot-bellied dwarf apparently a Negro is recumbent on his left side. His hand, now lost, was at his mouth. His right arm supports a nude, male (?) child, who is astride his back. Black details such as eyes and eyebrows, enhance the dwarf. On top of the dwarf's bald head is a hieroglyph that means "protection." All four edges of the base are purple-black.

The object is clearly magical – and possibly related to fertility – but precisely what function it was intended to serve is unclear.

Faience; late period; ca. 400 B.C. or later.
Height: 6.3 cm; width: 3.4 cm.

BIBLIOGRAPHY: Sultan pl. LXXXI: second row, third from left.   (J. D. C.)

237 Amulet

Two-finger amulets are known only from late times; this one is from a right hand.
Fingernails are delicately carved and joints are indicated by incisions on both back and front.
The medium, which has been identified as alabaster but which is more probably limestone, is a highly polished brown stone with small areas of yellow.

Probably limestone; late Dynastic.
Length: 10 cm.   (J. D. C.)

238   Head of an Old Man

The battered but still recognizable remains of a masterpiece of late Egyptian sculpture. It is the head of an elderly man doubtless from a standing statue. He has the usual shaven, almost ovoid head with very small, shrewd eyes and short mouth, the two combining to give him a harsh expression. He has a full, virtually double chin. On the back of the neck is a heavy fold of flesh and below it the remains of a back pillar.

It is curious that in both Egyptian and Greek sculpture no matter how terribly a superb piece of sculpture has been attacked it still retains quality as a work of art. Indeed, sometimes a fragment from one of these cultures acquires more appeal than the intact work.

Close grained gray granite with scattered areas of light red-tan mottling; ca. 300–250 B. C.

Height: 14 cm.

(J. D. C.)

239   Funerary Mask of a Man

This head, said to be from the Faiyum, was molded in plaster, and the eyes were inset with opaque white and black glass, a characteristic of the second century. The close-cropped hair is black; the skin, now pink, was certainly once red. Eyebrows, eyelashes, beard, and drooping moustache are black. As in most of these lifesize masks, which seem to have been made chiefly for Greek settlers in Egypt, there is some attempt at portraiture, but essentially the features are idealized or conventionalized.

At the lower back of the head is a roughly u-shaped support painted white and retaining traces of black decorations. This was intended to elevate the head, which was probably placed on the cover of a wooden coffin.

Plaster; Faiyum (?) probably A.D. 150–200.

Height: 19.5 cm.   (J. D. C.)

240 Fragment of a Shroud

Doubtless the lady for whom this unusually ornate white shroud was made was a Greek resident of Egypt. She is represented frontally with her hair dressed in a bun on top of her head and very small black curls outlining her face. Large brown eyes – underlined with bands of kohl – with prominent eyelashes are a striking feature of her pink-red face.

The ornate jewelry, modeled in gesso and gilded, includes a diadem set with imitation gems and painted light and dark red. On the chest are four necklaces, the first two in gilt, the third, also gilt, set with bullae enclosing red imitation stones. The fourth has large imitations of cabochon and lozenge gems in light and dark red.

Of the minor details certainly the most striking is the very unusual figure of the nude, dancing Aphrodite (?) grasping a palm branch. She is modeled in gilded gesso and the branch is painted brown and tan. This debased deity strikes an incongruous and frivolous air in this otherwise rather somber setting. At the right is a crane and below him a conventionalized bunch of grapes. Probably there was a glass of wine on the opposite side of the shroud, which, together with the grapes, was a symbol of Isis, whose worship was still prominent in Egypt. The intact shroud must have been a spectacular and somewhat garish affair but entirely in keeping with the exotic tastes of Greeks resident in Egypt.

The area directly behind her head is pale gray-blue duplicating the traditional background of the Faiyum portraits, and the lady's features are strongly suggestive of the Faiyum portraits in tempera executed around the middle of the fourth century.

Tempera on linen; ca. A.D. 325–350.
Height: 66 cm.; width: 29 cm.

(J. D. C.)

AMARNA RELIEFS

The group of twenty five reliefs, all of them in limestone of varying degrees of hardness, is of outstanding importance for the history of Egyptian art during the Amarna Period, late in Dynasty XVIII, ca. 1365–1353 B.C. It is apparent that they come from the temples and palaces at Akhenaten (Amarna), the romantic and ephemeral capital of Egypt built by order of Akhenaten, but where they were found is not known for certain. Since a few of these reliefs can be proved to come from the German excavations in the late 1930's at Hermopolis Magna (almost due west of Amarna), it is generally assumed that the Schimmel reliefs were also found, slightly later, at this site, and that they had been reused as foundation blocks by the architects of Ramesses II. The find seems to have consisted of a considerable number of reliefs showing a very wide range of quality, subjects and condition. Very few joins have been made, though in numerous instances it has been possible to infer a connection, if not a direct fit, between certain reliefs.

At a time prior to 1947 some of these reliefs were clumsily repainted in water paint, apparently in Upper Egypt. In some cases traces of ancient pigment remain; in others the modern paint has been removed. A considerable part of the find has already passed into public and private collections in Europe and America. Two fine examples, representing the king and queen, are in Hamburg and have been published recently (Jahrbuch der Hamburger Kunstsammlungen 7, 1962, 219 ff.). Those known to be owned in America have been published in John D. Cooney, Amarna Reliefs from Hermopolis in American Collections, The Brooklyn Museum (1965).

241 The King's Hand

One of the great reliefs of this group. The King has dropped a clump of fat on the offerings and his thumb and forefinger are shown just sprung apart from this action. Momentary poses of this nature are rare in earlier royal representations, but the Amarna artists delighted in them. The drawing of the hand is masterly.

Height: 23.5 cm.; width: 27.5 cm.

BIBLIOGRAPHY: ARAC, no. 2; Roeder, pl. 173, PC 2 and p. 404; AKKE, 27; Tadmor, no. 2, pl. 2; Akhenaten, pl. 40; I. Woldering, The Arts of Egypt (London, 1967), pl. 74; K. Michalowski, Art of Ancient Egypt, (New York, 1968), no. 442; Brooklyn, no. 147.   (J. D. C.)

One of the theoretical duties of the kings of Egypt was to officiate at every service for a god in any Egyptian temple. In practice, this duty had regularly to be delegated to priests, but in temple reliefs the king was always shown performing services for the gods. Here, in a unique scene, Akhenaten wrings the neck of a duck for the Aten and, to judge from the traces of another duck at the lower right, Nefertiti did the same. The active participation of the queen in these temple scenes was almost unknown until the Amarna Period when, suddenly, it became usual. The small cartouches on the king's arms are the Aten's.

Height: 24.5 cm.; width: 54.5 cm.

BIBLIOGRAPHY: ARAC, no. 9; Roeder, pl. 171, PC 13 and p. 404; AKKE, 28; Tadmor, no. 1, pl. 1; Akhenaten, pl. 20; Brooklyn, no. 118, where it is denied that the queen is, or was, represented holding a duck at the lower right.

(J. D. C.)

243   The King Offering

When this relief was discovered at Hermopolis Magna in 1939 it still preserved the right arm and hand of Akhenaten making a gesture connected with the offering ceremony. Since then someone has mutilated the representation.

The king wore the Blue Crown with long streamers, his most frequent headgear. The modelling of the body is typical of the best Amarna work. The ear lobe is pierced, the long neck has the conventionalized indications of flesh folds and great emphasis is given the collar bones.

Height: 21 cm.; width: 34.5 cm.

BIBLIOGRAPHY: ARAC, no. 7; Roeder, pl. 5, 255 (shown in its original state) and p. 383; AKKE, 29; Tadmor, no. 6, pl. 6; Akhenaten, pl. 38; Brooklyn, no. 117.   (J. D. C.)

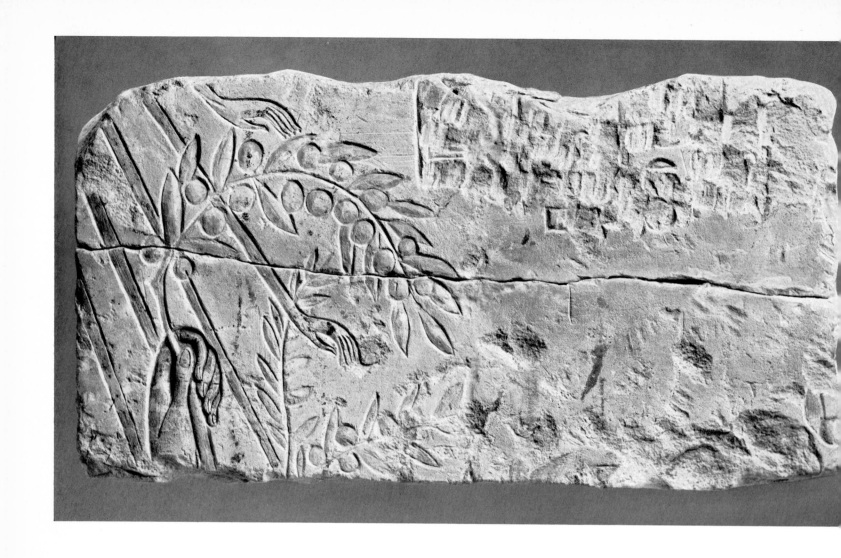

244   The King makes an Offering

A fragment from a scene where Akhenaten stood surrounded by the beneficent rays of the Aten to whom he
is offering. His beautifully rendered left hand clasps a
great branch of an olive tree heavily laden with fruit.
Representations of this fruit are very rare in New Kingdom art.

Height: 22 cm.; width: 44 cm.

BIBLIOGRAPHY: ARAC, no. 1; Roeder, pl. 170, PC 1 and
p. 403; AKKE, 30. Tadmor, no. 3, pl. 3; Akhenaten, pl. 93;
Brooklyn, no. 146.   (J. D. C.)

245   Throne within a Kiosk

A fragment from a great scene where the king sat within a kiosk of which only a part of the right support is preserved. The column was decorated with a cluster of pendant quails, pomegranates, lotus petals and strings of dates. At the extreme left is the back of the king's throne and, at the right, the lower part of a standing princess who stood behind the kiosk with her sisters.

Height: 23.5 cm.; width: 53.3 cm.

BIBLIOGRAPHY: ARAC, no. 62; Roeder, pl. 182, PC 51 and p. 405; AKKE, 31; Tadmor, no. 9, pl. 9.   (J. D. C.)

A relief which preserves parts of two separate scenes. At the left is a large figure of Akhenaten facing left. The inscription is connected with the scene to the right and reads "The nurse of Princess Ankh-es-en-pa-Aten, Tia". It was perhaps placed here to identify a small representation of Tia carved directly below the inscription, for the girl to the right is dressed with the trappings of a princess and must be Ankh-es-en-pa-Aten herself. She seems to have had a daughter by her father and, later, became the wife of Tutankhamun. She offers bread to the Aten; behind her is an elaborate heap of offerings.

Height: 22.2 cm.; width: 54 cm.

BIBLIOGRAPHY: ARAC, no. 10, Roeder, pl. 170, PC 12 and p. 404; AKKE, 32; Tadmor, no. 5, pl. 5; Akhenaten, pl. 78; K. Michalowski, Art of Ancient Egypt (New York, 1968), nos. 441 and 444; Brooklyn, no. 129; In the last reference the individual with the tray is identified as the nurse Tia.

(J. D. C.)

247 Royal Sisters

Two princesses, the elder perhaps Merit-Aten, are shown embracing in a domestic scene typical of Amarna art. The representation of the elder princess' torso in front view, unknown in Egyptian art before the Amarna Period, is found also in a few of the standstone blocks from the early Aten chapel at Karnak. It was probably introduced in an attempt to achieve depth, for there can be no doubt that the Amarna sculptors were greatly interested in the third dimension in relief. The relief has suffered extensive damage since its discovery at Hermopolis in 1939.

Height: 22 cm.; width: 28 cm.

BIBLIOGRAPHY: G. Roeder, Ein Jahrzehnt Deutscher Ausgrabungen in Ägypten (1951), pl. 4 (b), showing the earlier condition of the relief; ARAC, no. 16; Roeder, pl. 8, 218 and p. 386; AKKE, 33; Tadmor, no. 7, pl. 7; Akhenaten, pl. 75; Christiane D. Noblecourt and J. Yoyotte, Treasures of the Pharaohs (Geneva, 1968), p. 106; C. Aldred, Akhenaten (New York, 1968), pl. XI. Brooklyn, no. 130. In this last reference the larger person is identified as a nurse rather than an elder sister.   (J. D. C.)

At the right, a small part of the body of Nefertiti is preserved from what was probably a scene of the entire royal family worshipping in the temple. Behind the queen stood two princess of whom only the sandaled feet survive. Two male attendants kiss the ground in homage to their sovereigns and hold upright their fans. The sculptor has reversed the correct position of the men's hands and has also represented all four hands on the side of the body facing the spectator.

Height: 22.5 cm.; width: 54 cm.

BIBLIOGRAPHY: ARAC, no. 14; Roeder, pl. 171, PC 8, p. 404; AKKE, 34; Tadmor, no. 8, pl. 8; Akhenaten, pl. 37; I. Woldering, The Arts of Egypt (London, 1967), pl. 75. Brooklyn, no. 136 where the two (incomplete) ladies are declared not to be princesses.   (J. D. C.)

249 Purification of a Princess

This is an Amarna adaptation of a scene long standard in Egyptian religious representations. Traditionally, one or two gods flanked a king, pouring over him streams of holy water or symbols of life. Here a hand of the Aten which was the terminal of a long ray holds the jar in the upper left, pouring the purifying water over the young princess.

Height: 22.8 cm.; width: 47 cm.

BIBLIOGRAPHY: ARAC, no. 17; Roeder, pl. 172, PC 17 and p. 404; AKKE, 35; Tadmor, no. 4, pl. 4.   (J. D. C.)

250 Part of a Procession

These three men, each carrying a notched stick (or torch?), are clearly only a part of a long procession, for several other reliefs of the same subject are known both in this find and from the German excavations at Hermopolis. There, a relief was found where Akhenaten either gives or accepts one of these sticks. The scene was perhaps a celebration comparable to the Festival of Light or some harvest feast unknown to us.

Height: 22.8 cm.; width: 54 cm.

BIBLIOGRAPHY: ARAC, no. 55; Roeder, pl. 171, PC 14 and p. 404; AKKE, 36; Tadmor, no. 23 and pl. 23; Brooklyn, no. 75. (J. D. C.)

251 Attendants of the Royal Family

On their public appearances the royal family were invariably accompanied by groups of six ladies-in-waiting and gentlemen sunshade-bearers. While some of the details of the bodies show Amarna influence, the grouping of the ladies clasping fans and sashes follows the style of the reign of Amenhotep III.

Height: 23 cm.; width: 54 cm.

BIBLIOGRAPHY: ARAC, no. 18 c; Roeder, pl. 172, PC 15 and p. 404; AKKE, 37; Tadmor, no. 11, pl. 11; Akhenaten, pl. 35; Brooklyn, no. 137.   (J. D. C.)

Though related in subject, this relief contrasts vividly with the preceding relief. The trumpeter at the right duplicates other examples of about the same date. He seems to be playing for the group of peasant women, one of whom beats on a hand drum while her companions dance and gesture in excitement. Perhaps they are welcoming the king to the temple, a minor detail of a large composition.

Height: 24 cm.; width: 37.2 cm.

BIBLIOGRAPHY: ARAC, 44; Roeder, pl. 186, PC 76 and p. 406; AKKE, 38; Tadmor, no. 15 and pl. 15; Akhenaten, pl. 76.   (J. D. C.)

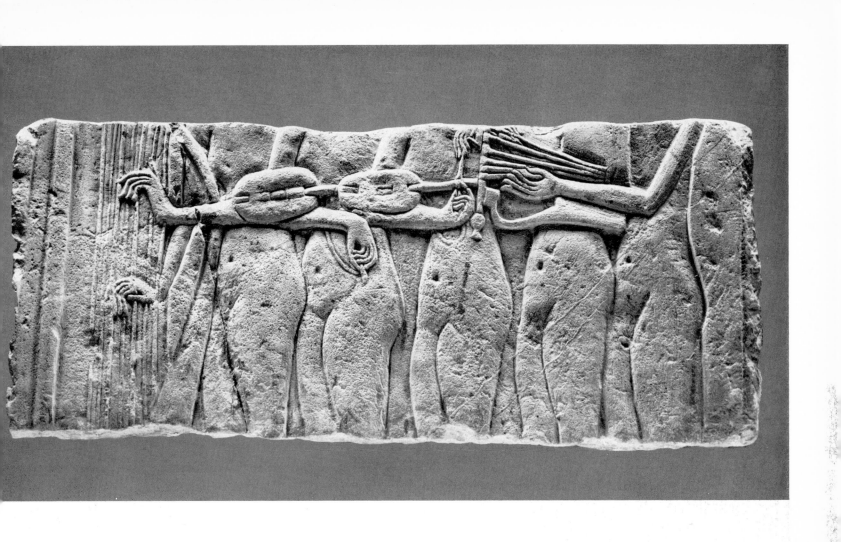

253   Court Musicians

In Amarna art these palace quintets are frequent. A harp
player is followed by two lute players each clasping a
plectrum, and they are followed by a lady without instrument who was perhaps a singer. At the end is the player
of the lyre. Despite the present appearance, these players
were probably shown with dresses. A splendid example
of a standard scene.

Height: 21 cm.; width: 53 cm.

BIBLIOGRAPHY: ARAC, no. 42; Roeder, pl. 171, PC 10 and
p. 404; AKKE, 39; Tadmor, no. 17, pl. 17; Akhenaten, pl.
74; Brooklyn, no. 74.   (J. D. C.)

254   Detail of a Procession

At the right are four heads of foreigners, one almost entirely destroyed. The men vary, in size, age and racial types. The four arms at the left clasping long shafts belong to still other soldiers or attendants of the king. The undulating, reed-like construction directly under the heads has never been clearly explained as no exact parallel is known. I have suggested a connection with the ceremony in the festival of the "Coming Forth of Min" in which an image of this god was carried on the shoulders of priests. The statue seems to have rested on a great openwork stretcher with the bearers standing within its framework, as here. But this identification is far from certain.

Height: 24.1 cm.; width: 53.5 cm.

BIBLIOGRAPHY: ARAC, no. 21; Roeder, pl. 170, PC 3 and p. 404; AKKE, 40. Tadmor, illustrated on back cover; Akhenaten, pl. 92; Brooklyn, no. 138. Here the curious horizontal construction under the heads is identified as ropes attached to the royal barge.   (J. D. C.)

255 Court Ladies at a Ceremony

Amarna representations of humans were frequently so epicene, with so many details of costume shifted from one sex to the other, that the determination of sex in this strange period, particularly in reliefs, is often complex. The people in this relief seem to be female, but the identification is far from certain. Nor is it possible to be certain what they are doing. They seem to be drinking from shallow bowls with their attention focused on some scene to the right. The skillfull, informal grouping of these people as a series of individuals is characteristic of Amarna art.

Height: 21.5 cm.; width: 53.5 cm.

BIBLIOGRAPHY: ARAC, no. 23; Roeder, pl. 170, PC 6 and p. 404; AKKE, 41; Tadmor, no. 10 and pl. 10; Akhenaten, pl. 39; Brooklyn, no. 139.   (J. D. C.)

256 Preparing the Royal Boat

One of the royal boats is moored on the east bank of the
Nile adjoining the palace. In the upper right is a section
of the palace garden, the plots shown in top view, the
plants in profile. A duck flies over the garden but is represented as under it or in front of it. The boat is of a type
known from the Amarna tombs and from a model in the
tomb of Tutankhamen, having a great central cabin with
a kiosk at one end. The structure so curiously drawn at
the right end of this boat is probably to be understood as
an open kiosk having a back and two sides, the front being
open. The back was decorated with a relief or painting of
Akhenaten in the traditional composition of the king
slaughtering his enemies. Nefertiti stands behind him.

Height: 23.3 cm.; width: 54.3 cm.

BIBLIOGRAPHY: ARAC, no. 50; Roeder, pl. 182, PC 55 and
p. 405; AKKE, 42; Tadmor, no. 21, pl. 21; Akhenaten, pl.
32; Brooklyn, no. 55.   (J.D.C.)

257 Attendants in the Royal Procession

Two ladies-in-waiting with fans stand in each chariot following behind the royal family. The upper part of the horse's head at the extreme right, the face of the second driver and the ladies' faces have been restored in part.

Height: 23.5 cm.; width: 54.7 cm.

BIBLIOGRAPHY: ARAC, no. 33; Roeder, pl. 172, PC 18 and p. 404; AKKE, 43; Tadmor, no. 13, pl. 13; Akhenaten, pl. 28; Brooklyn, no. 73.　　　　　　　　(J. D. C.)

A relief of great complexity and interest. A group of horses represented in violent motion and lacking any indication of harnesses. The only plausible explanation of this magnificent composition is that it represents horses let loose for exercise on the desert plain to the east of Amarna. This relief is of the greatest importance as a prototype of the complex battle scenes which were developed by the Ramesside relief sculptors.

Height: 23.2 cm.; width: 49.5 cm.

BIBLIOGRAPHY: ARAC, no. 25; Roeder, pl. 216, PC 78 and p. 405; AKKE, 44; Tadmor, no. 19, pl. 19; Brooklyn, no. 148; Here the subject is identified as a military scene, perhaps a surprise attack on the picket line.   (J. D. C.)

259 Waiting Horses

A span of horses waiting with their chariots. This subject, almost commonplace in Amarna reliefs, is given great vitality by the movement of a horse who lowers his head to rub or bite on his leg. A splendid representation of a rapid, momentary action. The slender object overlapping the tail of the horse may be the lower part of a quiver.

Height: 23 cm.; width: 52 cm.

BIBLIOGRAPHY: ARAC, no. 27; Roeder, pl. 171, PC 7 and p. 404; AKKE, 45; Tadmor, no. 18 and pl. 18; Akhenaten, pl. 33; Brooklyn, no. 78.   (J. D. C.)

Two large-scale heads of Negroes with prothaganous skulls are skillfully modelled in soft limestone. The staff passing in front of them must be from a standard; it is rectangular in section. A small portion of still another head survives at the left. It is likely that these soldiers formed part of the royal bodyguard. The completed composition must have been on a vast scale.

Height: 21.6 cm.; width: 46.7 cm.

BIBLIOGRAPHY: ARAC, no. 22; Roeder, pl. 170, PC 4 and p. 404; AKKE, 46; Tadmor, no. 16 and pl. 16; Akhenaten, pl. 94.   (J. D. C.)

261   Scene of Chariots

This is not, as at first glance appears, one of the rare representations of horses with rider. As it is now preserved the relief has elements of two separate details of a procession, the heads of the two horses belonging to a chariot represented far to the right while the man is apparently the driver of a span of horses preceding the horses which are preserved on the left side of this relief.

In front of the man are two small strands, possibly parts of the reins. The face of this man is curiously un-Egyptian in feeling. Here again the great scale of the relief infers a prominent location necessitating the service of an expert sculptor. All worked areas were repainted in pink-red.

Height: 22 cm.; width: 26.5 cm.

BIBLIOGRAPHY: ARAC, no. 28; Roeder, pl. 176, PC 16; Brooklyn, no. 79.   (J. D. C.)

262 Animals Foraging

Antelopes and gazelles are shown on a sloping base line probably indicating a hilly desert area. The animals in the lower right are biting on some vegetation. The two small legs which appear on the upper right edge of the relief are probably from a representation of a gazelle rearing to eat from a tree or bush.

Height: 23 cm.; width: 52 cm.

BIBLIOGRAPHY: ARAC, no. 40; Roeder, pl. 171, PC 8 and p. 404; AKKE, 48; Tadmor, no. 20, pl. 20; Brooklyn, no. 149. (J. D. C.)

263   Fishing Scene

At the left a man stands on the bank of a marsh seemingly holding up a long spear on which is impaled a fish and a duck represented just above the fish. Both fish are bultis. In the water the buds and flowers of the lotus are shown in profile, the leaf in top view. The interpretation of this scene would be almost impossible without a parallel composition in ivory from the tomb of Tutankhamen. There, as doubtless also on this relief, the king is seated on a splendid chair within a hunting-blind. With bow and arrow he spears fish and fowl while his beaters collect and display the royal kill. A rare subject in Egyptian art.

Height: 22 cm.; width: 53.3 cm.

BIBLIOGRAPHY: ARAC, no. 41; Roeder, pl. 174, PC 35 and p. 405; AKKE, 49; Tadmor, illustrated on front cover; Brooklyn, no. 150.   (J. D. C.)

264 Grape-vine

The vine was a favorite subject of Amarna sculptors, and numerous examples have been found at Amarna and Hermopolis. An unusual detail of this relief is the hollow area surrounding the bunch of grapes. The result is that the grapes appear almost to be in the round.

Height: 23 cm.; width: 42 cm.

BIBLIOGRAPHY: ARAC, no. 59; Roeder, pl. 170, PC 5 and p. 404; AKKE, 50; Tadmor, no. 22, pl. 22; Akhenaten, pl. 42; Brooklyn, no. 83. (J. D. C.)

265 A Field of Wheat

A subject in raised relief and of the greatest naturalism. The subject was already old in Egyptian art when this relief was created, but for the first time wheat is here represented as it appears in the field. Possibly the scene is connected with the coronation ceremony, but this is very conjectural.

Height: 23 cm.; width: 52 cm.

BIBLIOGRAPHY: ARAC, no. 57; AKKE, 51; Tadmor, no. 24, pl. 24; Akhenaten, pl. 43; Brooklyn, 93.   (J. D. C.)

LIST OF PHOTOGRAPHS

All photographs were made by Otto Nelson with exception of the following nos.:

13, 43, 50a, 72b, 75, 77, 86, 89a, 110, 111, 121a, 135, 140, 176, 191, 201, 204, 209, 211, 229, 233   by Werner Forman

32b, 32c, 33, 36, 39, 131   by Dieter Johannes

35, 83, 84, 96, 97, 99   by Michael Nedzweski

15, 20, 26 bis   by Otto Pilco

3, 4, 21, 27, 63, 67, 70, 100, 122, 162, 174, 200   by Dietrich Widmer

76, 92, 120, 121b, 129, 130, 155b, 157, 203, 237   by Robert Zucker

56, 64, 124b, 142, 152   by The Metropolitan Museum of Art

The drawings for nos. 12, 54, 123, and 128 were made by Grace Freed Muscarella, for no. 15 by Suzanne Chapman.

ERRATA AND ADDENDA

Dedication to J. Cooney: p. 2 P 3, line 1: indebeted should be indebted.

Credits: Vaugn should be Vaughn.

Cat. no. 6: line 1: so should be to.

Cat. no. 16: BIBLIOGRAPHY: Propyläen Kunstgeschichte I: K. Schefold, Die Griechen und ihre Nachbarn (Berlin, 1967), 205, Taf. 149 (A. Greifenhagen).

Cat. no. 19: P 3, line 1: related of should be related to.

Cat. no. 25 bis: BIBLIOGRAPHY: line 9: omit parenthesis before had . . . and after before.

Cat. no. 28: line 8: caeducei should be caducei.

Cat. no. 36: P 3, line 6: (Syme) should be (Symes).

Cat. no. 38: P 2, line 2: (inv. 1947.246); should be (inv. 1947.246; . . . Vickers).

Cat. no. 39: P 2, line 2: Beş should be Bes.

Cat. no. 40: line 8: θϱῦνυς shoud be θϱῆνυς.

Cat. no. 47: P 3, line 7: goattee should be goatee.

Cat. no. 48: Papposilenos should be Pappasilenos.

Cat. no. 53: last P: Boetian should be Boeotian.

Cat. no. 56: BIBLIOGRAPHY: JDI should be JdI.

Cat. no. 58: BIBLIOGRAPHY: H. Hoffmann und should be H. Hoffmann and.

Cat. no. 73: last line: Achemenian should be Achaemenian.

Cat. no. 74: P 2, line 5: posession should be possession.
James Loeb died in Murnau, Germany, in 1933; he never returned to the United States. The stalk of wheat passed into the possession of his stepson Mr. J. W. Hambüchen.
BIBLIOGRAPHY: P. Wolters, in Die Antike 6 (1930) 284 ff.

Cat. no. 92: CREDIT: J.C. should be J.D.C.

Cat. no. 109 bis: P 1, line 6: claspes should be clasps.

Cat. no. 118: P 2, line 1: heards should be heads.

Cat. no. 123: P 1, line 3: should read: ". . . horns, ears, neckband, ears and lip . . ." Page 4, P 5, line 1: Tarkodemos should be Tarkondemos.
Page 6, line 21: Yaziliyaka should be Yazilikaya.

Cat. no. 125: page 3, line 9: Eflatum should be Eflatun.

Cat. no. 129: P 3, line 1: mellennium should be millennium.

Cat. no. 130: HEADING: Lobed Headed should be Lobe Headed.

Cat. no. 131: BIBLIOGRAPHY: Fund should be Funde.

Cat. no. 132: BIBLIOGRAPHY: hetitische should be hethitische.

Cat. no. 136: BIBLIOGRAPHY: Fouille should be Fouilles.

Cat. no. 139: P 2, line 15: deliniated should be delineated.

Cat. no. 152 bis P 3, line 2: smoothe should be smooth.

Cat. no. 156: P 3, line 3: motiv should be motif.
BIBLIOGRAPHY: Memoirés should be Mémoires.

Cat. no. 165: P 2, line 2: is said should be are said.

Egyptian Introduction: line 4: (not incorrectly) should be (not correctly).

Cat. no. 177: Height 9.2 cm.

Cat. no. 183: P 2, line 3: Kusae should be Cusae.

Cat. no. 189: BIBLIOGRAPHY: Akhenaton should be Akhenaten.

Cat. no. 215: line 3: horizontal should be vertical.

Cat. no. 227: CAPTION should read: "XXX Dynasty to early Ptolemaic Period."

Cat. no. 229: P 2, line 1: crudeley should be crudely.

Cat. no. 255: line 9: skillfull should be skillful.

Cat. no. 264: HEADING: Grape-vine should be Grapevine.

237 bis   Sculptor's Model

An exceptional and interesting sculpture. It seems to be a studio model or study for a statue of a man in voluminous robes. The cylindrical form of the body, almost unknown in pre-Persian Egyptian art, was typical of Mesopotamian sculpture at a very early date. Soft limestone.

4th century B.C. · Height 23 cm.

BIBLIOGRAPHY: B. V. Bothmer, Egyptian Sculpture of the Late Period (Brooklyn, 1960) no. 86. (Already published in the first catalogue under no. 100.)
(J.D.C.)